COMPUTERS THAT THINK ?

COMPUTERS THAT THINK?

THE SEARCH FOR ARTIFICIAL INTELLIGENCE

MARGARET O. HYDE

ENSLOW PUBLISHERS
Bloy Street and Ramsey Avenue
Box 777
Hillside, New Jersey 07205

Library of Congress Cataloging in Publication Data

Hyde, Margaret Oldroyd, 1917-
Computers that think.

Bibliography: p.
Includes index.
Summary: Describes artificial intelligence, which is that branch of computer science devoted to programming computers to carry out tasks that would require intelligence if they were performed by humans.
1. Artificial intelligence.
[1. Computers. 2. Artificial intelligence] I. Title.

Q335.H85 001.53'5 81-12614

ISBN 0-89490-055-2, hardcover
ISBN 0-89490-079-X, paperback AACR2

Printed in the United States of America

10 9 8 7 6 5 4 3 2 1

For Emily Goodrich Hyde

CONTENTS

The author wishes to thank the many people who contributed to this book. Samuel Burstein, Ph.D., Associate Professor of Mathematical Science at New York University, was especially helpful.

1.

MICE, CHESS PLAYERS, & ARTIFICIAL INTELLIGENCE

Computers that read books for the blind are already changing the world in which they live. Machines that can recognize your voice, respond to your spoken command, and call you by name exist—mainly in laboratories. Researchers are developing computer programs that can read news stories and write summaries of them. They can assemble data about a person's illness and make a diagnosis. Someday, such computers may be commonplace. These are the "smart machines," machines that exhibit what some scientists call artificial intelligence.

Most of today's computers are not considered to be intelligent even though they can perform more than millions of additions in a second and the human brain takes one second or more to do a single addition. While speed gives computers great power for keeping track of airline reservations and dealing with problems of weather forecasting, they are primitive in areas of abstract reasoning, recognizing patterns, and language ability. A human masters many problems each day that would be difficult for a computer expert to program into a sophisticated machine.

The people who founded the science of artificial intelligence about 25 years ago feel that it is still in its infancy. Some describe it as a science that does not know where it is going, one that is following an uncharted path in a murky sea.

It is hard to describe artificial intelligence to someone. Most people are bewildered when asked what it is, and many who have a rough idea about what it is admit that their knowledge is vague.

Even experts disagree about the meaning of artificial intelligence and whether or not some of today's computers can rightly be called intelligent machines. They do agree that artificial intelligence is that branch of computer science devoted to programming computers to carry out tasks that would require intelligence if the tasks were performed by humans. Computers are the tools of artificial intelligence, and it is computer programs that enable these tools to do things that would require intelligence if done by people. Some of these programs help in the understanding of learning, problem solving, human personality, and creativity. Some enable robots to simulate our senses of vision and touch. "Artificial assistants" are finding their way into industry in the form of computer programs that enable computers to serve as consultants to humans faced with difficult decisions.

Experts believe that computers will eventually be able to solve many kinds of problems that human beings cannot solve. People will look to them for help in managing the complex world of the future. Even today, artificial intelligence researchers conduct a variety of programs aimed at increasing the ability of computers to solve problems, communicate with people, and interact with the physical world. New programs may use artificial intelligence methods to design integrated electronic circuits which are becoming impossibly complex for the human intellect.

Will computers ever outsmart people? Will scientists ever be able to build an ultra-intelligent machine? Herbert A. Simon, a founder of artificial intelligence and Nobel prize winner for his research on decision-making, sees no great reason to fear this kind of knowledge. He suggests that human beings sometimes use power for good and sometimes they misuse it. But if one has to choose between knowledge and ignorance, knowledge is better.

Researchers approach the problem of understanding and simulating human intelligence through two routes. One route studies the human brain and examines the parts of the nervous system that correspond roughly to parts of a computer system. In this approach, there is an attempt to define precisely what happens when humans think. Computers are used primarily for exploring ideas. For example, Herbert A. Simon works in the field of artificial intelligence to gain a better insight into the thought processes of human beings. He wants to know how the human mind works, and he concentrates on how decisions get made. The other approach to artificial intelligence is to try to make computers more intelligent irrespective of how the brain works.

No matter how the goals of the researchers are reached, you can be certain that many people who are alive today will see the world transformed largely through new advances that are based on work in the field of artificial intelligence. Marvin L. Minsky, a leader in the field of artificial intelligence, believes that a machine with the general intelligence of an average human being *will* be built and it will be followed by even more intelligent machines. While not everyone agrees, most experts think that artificial intelligence programs and human thought have much to learn from each other. The possibilities are staggering.

While artificial intelligence is a branch of science in its infant state, "the computer revolution" is in full swing. It has been compared with the industrial revolution in which muscle power was replaced by steam power and by machines that did the work of many hands, with greater precision and accuracy. Electronic computers supplement some aspects of human mental power, and they are getting "smarter" at what some people consider a frightening rate.

There are futurists who predict that new computer technology will bring improvements that are from 100,000 to a million times greater than the improvements that were made before the 1980's. Some people have already begun to work from their homes at least several days a week by using computers that are connected to their offices. Tremendous stores of information are available to them through the use of data banks. A data bank, or data base, is a collection of libraries of data containing such things as bibliographies and abstracts of books; articles on science, law, medicine, literature, history, and the arts; and stock market quotations. By 1981, more than 450 data bases were available in the United States. This so-called telecommuting, along with teleshopping and teleconferencing, are just the beginning of exciting and amazing things to come.

Progress in artificial intelligence may enable us to explain human thought by the use of computers and computer programs, and many people will find themselves reconsidering what it means to be human. They may view themselves as colleagues of intelligent machines that augment their own reasoning capacities. Computers that think may also expand the capacity of people to see, hear, feel, and smell, providing

---

In space, robots will take over an increasing number of functions.

—Jet Propulsion Laboratory

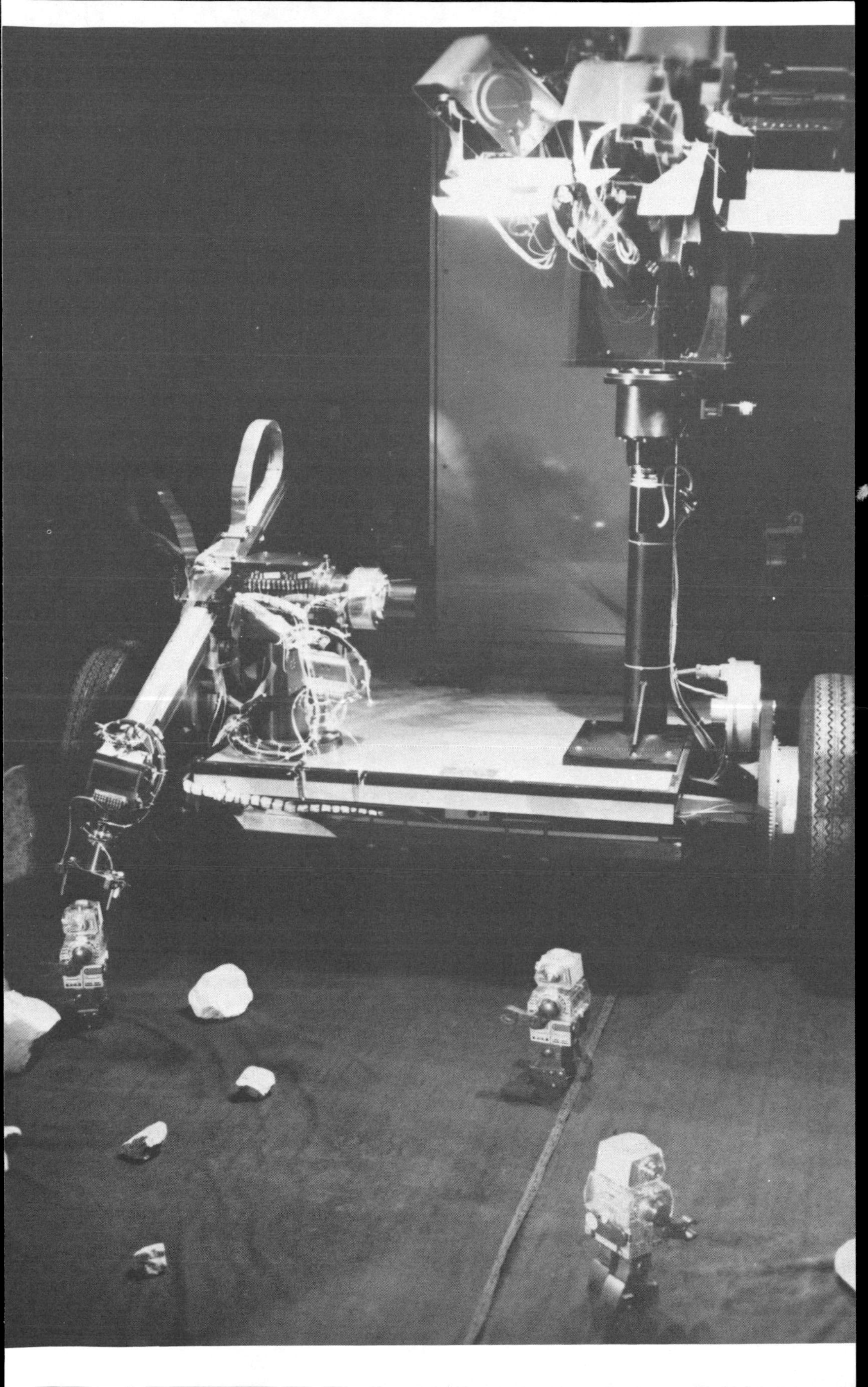

wonderful experiences that are beyond those even being dreamed about today.

Artificial intelligence may be needed to solve problems of the future that are beyond the capacity of human minds. People will be the programmers and organizers of projects for the intellectual computers which will satisfy human needs. At least a minimal level of control will almost certainly be built into future computers, but education and knowledge are the keys to such control. The topic of whether or not computers might someday develop a self-awareness and "take over" is discussed later in this book.

Today's researchers in artificial intelligence have already applied what they have learned about human thought to some practical things such as "intelligent robots," game playing, and script reading. Many people have learned to play chess with the help of a chess computer. Some of these machines can play at many levels including one that will teach a beginner. Messages flash to the learner from a seemingly human brain. Sometimes the computer lets the player win and sometimes it makes the person lose. If the human is uncertain of the next move, the computer suggests one. It is a patient teacher when playing a beginner's game. The same computer can play games that will keep the attention of an expert.

About 15 years ago, many people were certain that no computer would ever be able to beat a good chess player. By the end of the 1970's, well programmed computers could outplay nearly 100% of the world's chess players and could play high-level games with each other. A computer with high-speed microelectronic circuits can evaluate some 5,000 positions per second. The human chess players who outwit such computers appear to do so by considering a small number of promising moves in original ways. They use a kind of intuition that even they do not understand.

Most electronic servants that help to avert airline disasters, help to cook meals, prospect for oil, keep track of money in the bank, and print newspapers are problem solvers. All computers use programs that tell the computer what to do. Those that do not involve artificial intelligence always follow a step-by-step method provided by the programmers of the computer. They are programmed in such a way that they carry out specific tasks using the predefined methods.

Artificial intelligence programs are designed to be as general as possible so that, given a program and the knowledge relevant to solving a problem, the computer should be able to work out a method of doing it. Researchers in artificial intelligence try to create programs that not only work out step-by-step methods for solving problems but also, once the method is defined, carry out the steps. Artificial intelligence researchers are trying to get computers to link common characteristics of separate facts.

Micromice that run mazes are some of the most appealing examples of computers that appear to exhibit a kind of artificial intelligence. These artificial rodents can "feel" their way and memorize the correct path after two tries in a maze. On the third run, Moonlight Special, the micromouse pictured on pages 18 and 19, can crawl from start to finish without making a wrong turn or bumping into a wall. Its "brain" is a micro-computer that completely maps the maze in two passes and makes 33 decisions each time the gray, fiberglass animal runs a 20-foot-square maze.

Moonlight Special is just one of many electronic mice designed for the Amazing Micro-Mouse Maze Contest in which engineers ran their "toys" through an unknown maze by use of

"Moonlight Special," a micromouse, navigates the Amazing Micro-Mouse Maze.
—Battelle Pacific Northwest Laboratories

"Moonlight Special" was made by six engineers who "moonlighted" to create this micromouse. *—Battelle Pacific Northwest Laboratories*

the logic and memories within each mouse. Thousands of such mice have run in trial contests from coast to coast in the United States, and some participated in a national contest that was run at a computer conference in New York.

Moonlight Special, the mouse in the picture, is the product of about 500 hours of work by six engineers who "moonlighted" to create it at the Battelle Pacific Northwest Laboratories. The mouse's energy is supplied by a rechargeable battery pack that frees it from wires and external power sources. It glides through the maze on two wheels that are driven by its motors. The motors rotate the wheels an exact distance for each pulse of electricity, and the microprocessor counts the pulses to keep track of the distance covered. Light beams are used to identify pathways in the maze, and the computer "brain" interrupts the light beam and stops the mouse when it approaches the walls.

The rodent's memory includes four small chips, each 1" by 1½", for the storage of information. Two chips contain Moonlight Special's program, all the information it needs to function and control its response under given conditions. It is these chips, for example, that produce the signal needed to make the mouse turn left when it encounters a wall either in front of it or to the right side. When the battery pack is turned off, information in the temporary microprocessor is erased. Then Moonlight Special is ready to learn the course of the next run.

The goal of artificial intelligence to increase capability is especially interesting in the world of robots. A great deal of research in this field concerns adding "eyes," "hands," and "feet" (in the form of wheels) to make them function in more helpful ways. These machines may not look like the robots of science fiction, and they may not see the way people do, but they can recognize patterns and accomplish some amazing tasks. Imagine robots that can stamp steel panels into complete automobile bodies. Such robots are part of a plan for the not-too-distant future.

These are just some of the many exciting applications of artificial intelligence. Computers do not yet communicate well with people because they need their own special languages. (You may know something about BASIC and FORTRAN, popular computer languages.) But computers are learning to communicate in natural language. In this and many other areas of this branch of computer science, exciting advances are being made.

Although some people feel that computers that think may cause nothing but trouble, most everyone who understands the progress in artificial intelligence is eagerly looking forward to the day when computers can solve an increasing number of the world's problems that cannot be solved by human beings.

2.

THINKING MACHINE OR IDIOT COMPUTER?

People have been arguing for many years about whether or not computers are intelligent machines. "Can the computer think?" has been asked again and again. A book called *The Thinking Machine* was published in 1962 to describe a "new breed of machine" known as the computer. These machines were described as among the most expensive necessities yet invented, costing hundreds of thousands of dollars apiece. Today anyone may own a personal computer costing just several hundred dollars that can "think" as well as one of the old giants. It balances the checkbooks, plans the menus, plays games with its owner, and is a good teaching tool for the children. One can program it with ease, and it communicates with the programmer to point out an error. The computer never makes a mistake, provided its electrical circuits are properly functioning. The error is always human. Sometimes the computer seems so smart that it is irritating—until one remembers that without the programmer the computer cannot do anything at all.

However, John Pfeiffer, the well-known author of *The*

Common computers, such as the one used in this drug store, are usually not considered to be thinking machines. *—Courtesy of IBM*

Thinking Machine states, "of course computers think." Pfeiffer's reasoning is as follows: Computers do for the brain what other machines do for the muscles. Bulldozers do work and no one argues that point. They do not work without the help of a person, but they work. "Computers do think," he says. They do not store information or perform memory searches without the help of a programmer, but they do think.

Stanley L. Englebardt wrote a book called *Computers* that was published about the same time as *The Thinking Machine.* Under the title on the paperback edition one finds the following: " 'Thinking machines' and their fantastic abilities—from language translation to the exploration of space." In this case "thinking machines" is placed in quotation marks. In the chapter titled "Can They Think?" this author notes that no computer has come up with a totally original thought that was not first asked for through programming. But he also notes that many serious scientists believe that machines may be capable of going beyond their designers.

Some of today's computers possess a degree of originality. Certainly some computers simulate a portion of the human thinking process. In some areas, they outperform the human brain.

"Are computers a species?" asks John G. Kemeny, an outstanding computer expert who is co-inventor of the widely used computer language known as BASIC. In his book *Man and the Computer,* which was written a decade after the two books mentioned earlier, he considers the computer as to characteristics often attributed to living things and notes that they show ability to communicate, that they show individuality, and that some computers exhibit a sort of metabolism. He also suggests that a robot might exhibit metabolism, which is defined as the ability to perform a chemical change in matter to generate energy.

Computer-directed robots can be equipped with power cells and can be instructed to go to electric outlets periodically, plug themselves in, and recharge their batteries.

Living things have the characteristic of being able to reproduce. A robot might fit the criteria of reproduction by assembling a new robot. In the area of sense organs, some robots see and listen in a primitive sort of way. There is little question about their having locomotion.

Some of the above comparisons seem ridiculous to many people, but Dr. Kemeny states that there is no question in his mind about the intelligent quality of computers—because they could be programmed in such a way that they would do well on intelligence tests.

However, not everyone agrees how well computers might fare on intelligence tests. Many of today's experts still classify them as electro-mechanical idiots. They point out that intelligent animals developed their brains over a very long period of time compared with the time scale of the computer world. In some areas, computers are far ahead of human brains. While the computer calculates numerical problems much faster than the brain, the capacity of the brain for handling visual data is far superior to the computer's. Some of the most sophisticated computers can process data at the rate of about one trillion bits of information a second. The overall data-processing capacity of the brain has been estimated at about 10 trillion bits of information per second. However, many experts believe the speed of computers will surpass that of the human brain in this kind of activity very shortly. But can computers be programmed to use vision more efficiently, or to reason? Will these machines become more intelligent in the near future?

One of the problems in considering whether or not computers are intelligent is the confusion over a definition of intelligence. Even though everyone has some idea of what is meant by intelligence, it is difficult to be specific. Would you consider a 17-year-old who can speak some French, do college-level calculus, and play checkers and chess well enough to beat most of the people in the town as intelligent? Most people would, even before testing his or her qualifications against the dictionary definition.

According to *The Random House Dictionary,* "Intelligence is the capacity for reasoning, understanding, and for similar forms of mental activity; aptitude in grasping truth, facts, meaning." Now instead of considering the 17-year-old, suppose a computer is the subject of this discussion. Do you still consider him, her, or it, intelligent?

Many people who become upset at the idea of a machine being intelligent are quite willing to accept the idea of intelligence in a variety of animals. According to one definition of animal intelligence, it is "the ability to adapt to changes in environmental conditions through changes in behavior." On the basis of this definition, even a simple, one-celled animal shows some intelligence for it moves away from some stimuli and toward others.

Many of the actions that humans consider intelligent in animals are cases of inborn ingenuity. The behavior patterns of birds that fly long migratory routes and of insects that make slaves of other insects are written in their genes. This is not what most people mean by intelligence.

It seems obvious that many animals, especially mammals, can actually learn a great deal. Almost everyone is familiar with the tricks that can be taught to dogs and other pets. Cats are not exceptionally intelligent when compared to apes, but some cats learn to turn on a water faucet when they want a drink. A sea lion can be trained to blow horns in such a way that it plays

The average chimpanzee can easily be taught a variety of skills.

—Lincoln Park Zoo/Bud Bertog

Yankee Doodle. Actually, the sea lion has been trained to blow the horns in a certain order by being rewarded with fish after playing a proper note. Through a long series of rewarding desired behavior with a treat of fish, the trainer has taught the sea lion to play a tune that pleases people. However, the sea lion would play the horns in the same order even if the horns all made exactly the same sound.

The average chimpanzee can easily be taught to eat with a fork and to use tools such as a saw, hammer, and screwdriver. Chimps have been taught to count up to five and how to insert the pegs in toy puzzles. Some chimps learn the correct way to put square, round, and triangular blocks in the proper holes faster than very young children.

As long ago as 1925, studies showed that apes are reasonably intelligent. Experimenters suspended fruit so that the apes could not reach it. In such experiments, many apes carried a box to place beneath the fruit, stood on the box and reached the fruit. In one experiment an ape exhibited a behavior that was even more intelligent. The animal spotted a bunch of bananas outside his cage. After many tries, he inserted one bamboo shaft inside another to make a pole long enough to reach them.

In other experiments chimps have stacked boxes under suspended bananas and, when they still could not reach the bananas, have used a stick to knock them down. Psychologists point out that many three-year-old children cannot learn to stack blocks to build a tower. However, chimpanzees are usually considered to be about as bright as a three-year-old person.

Some chimps have been taught to use computer consoles to communicate with humans and in certain cases, with each other. Duane Rumbaugh, a researcher working at Yerkes Regional Primate Center, taught the chimp Lana to communicate

Chimpanzees are usually considered to be about as bright as a three-year-old person. *—Lincoln Park Zoo/Bud Bertog*

with humans by punching out messages on a computer-like console to form 256 words and to use words in combination to release food from a vending machine and to obtain companionship or entertainment.

In testing any animal on a standard intelligence test, it is only fair to take into account the fact that the tests were designed to measure certain qualities in people. Christopher Evans in his popular book *The Micro Millenium* suggests that one use the number one million as the average intelligent quotient for human beings rather than 100. Judging animals on such a scale, slow learning humans would have an IQ of 999,970 and very, very bright ones would be in the 1,000,070 range. A dog or cat would rate about 300,000 to 500,000 and an ape might score in the 800,000 range. Evans rates the brightest of today's computers somewhere around 3000 on his scale, a position below the fish. He points out that this is not to show how stupid the computers are, but how very magnificent human beings and animals that have perceptual discrimination are.

A computer is not intelligent or "clever like a fox," an animal that can do intuitive thinking, make bright guesses and leap to conclusions and determine all its own instructions without programming provided by another animal.

Some of the "smart" machines have been compared with toddlers who are learning to speak and stack blocks, but human capability for intelligence is so diverse that it is extremely difficult to measure.

The tests used to measure the mental ability of human beings include a variety of categories such as abstract reasoning, verbal reasoning, numerical reasoning, space relations and perception. Computers rate higher in some of these areas than in others, but they are improving in almost every way.

Computers have long rated high with regard to some of the characteristics that go with intelligence. Few would question the ability of a computer to make decisions based on information or the ability of a computer to solve problems. Some chess computers improve with every game, exhibiting an ability to learn from experience.

Many people who find it difficult to accept the idea that computers can exhibit intelligence are quick to emphasize that a computer can only do what it is told to do. Instructions must be stored in every computer in the form of a program. Today the program can include instructions for learning and adapting to the outside world. Computers that store a vast body of knowledge can be programmed to learn from their own experiences and to make decisions based on these experiences and their own stores of information. These computers can manipulate symbols to reach logical conclusions based on information provided by the programmers. But even the smartest computers are a long way from being able to understand the way humans do.

A famous test for computer intelligence was suggested by Alan Turing, an English mathematician, more than a quarter of a century ago. In this test, a person is in a room where there are two computer terminals. One terminal is connected to a human being and the other is connnected to a computer. The person performing the test does not know which terminal is connected with the computer and which is connected with the other person. He or she uses the terminals to type out questions that the person and the computer answer by machines that print the answers in an identical typeface. The person performing the test has the task of determining which is which.

A sophisticated computer might carry on a good conversation with the person who is to act as the judge in the

Turing test. Executives have been known to mistake their computers for their associates. For example, a man and a woman are carrying on a conversation via a computer network. The man leaves the room without telling the woman and the computer continues to converse with her. A brief period may pass before the computer is recognized as not being her associate. However, this is not considered to be a true example of passing the Turing test. If the woman were alerted to the necessity of deciding whether or not she was talking to a person, she might have recognized the computer sooner.

Consider the Turing test in the context of a chess game. Peter J. Sandiford, director of operations research for Trans-Canadian Air Lines, arranged an experiment in which two students played chess with computers when they thought they were playing with one another. The referees and the chess computers were together in a separate room, listening to the comments of the boy and girl players. The referees kept the score and helped to operate the computers. The charade reached its conclusion without either person suspecting the true nature of his or her opponent. The students were astonished when they were brought into the room with the robot chess players. They found it difficult to believe they had not been playing chess with each other.

Suppose a chess grand master cannot tell whether or not the opponent is a person or a computer? Would this be an example of passing the Turing test? International grand masters have occasionally lost to computers, but this is a limited display of machine intelligence.

Turing anticipated that his test would not be passed by machines before the beginning of the twenty-first century. To pass the test, a computer would have to store a huge amount of knowledge about the real world. By 1980 it was estimated that a large computer could store about 1/10,000,000 of the information stored in an intelligent brain. Auxiliary memory systems could increase this amount to a trillion bits of data making the capacity about 1/10 that of a human brain. But even if the amount is increased to the point where the amounts of information are equal, the computer would have to learn which bits of information are important.

The human brain has a complex system of linking the information that it holds in storage. Think about how much information you would have to include in directions for teaching a child to ride a bicycle. You can instruct a person with just a few words. A similar computer program would not be so simple. And what about the problem of emotion? In some laboratories, artificial intelligence researchers are beginning to try to teach computers to deal with information that involves emotions, but most doubt that machines will ever "feel" very deeply.

Certainly, computers are far from being intelligent in the full sense. The nagging question about whether or not the machines will reach the point where they will become so intelligent that they will take over from man continues, but for all its amazing performances, the computer is still a dumb machine and humans can still pull the plug.

3.

ON/OFF IS ALL THE COMPUTER KNOWS

In order to have some understanding of what is happening in the world of artificial intelligence, it helps to have a basic idea about how a computer functions and how computers are evolving.

Again and again one hears the expression, "The computer can do only what you tell it to do." In other words, a computer cannot do anything that has not been programmed into its memory. Even though a chess computer may play better chess than the person who designed the programs, the better game played by the computer is accounted for by its attributes of enormous speed and accuracy.

While many young children can write programs for computers, most adults find everything about computers very mystifying. Actually, a program consists of a set of instructions that causes it to run through a series of tasks. Only a computer program can tell a computer what to do, even though, as mentioned earlier, some sophisticated computers can be programmed to modify their own programs.

Computers have three main sections each dedicated to

perform a different function. There is a central processing unit that carries out logical and arithmetic tasks. This part is the organizer, the part that controls the sequence of all the operations.

A second section is the memory where information is stored. There are generally two types of information stored in the memory: the program, or instructions, to be carried out by the computer and the data upon which the program acts.

A third section is the input/output system, which enables the computer to interact with the user. There are many kinds of input and output devices. The keyboard and the card reader, which converts holes in punched cards into electrical impulses, are popular forms of input devices. Screens similar to those on television sets, printers, magnetic tape drives, and spoken voice are popular kinds of output devices. The output of a computer may be connected with data banks, where large amounts of information are stored and transferred to individual terminals in remote places.

All three sections described above are commonly known as hardware. Software is the term used for the set of computer programs and for other programming material associated with using the computer.

The basic building block of the computer is a switching device called a transistor. The smallest unit of information that a computer can use is one binary digit, represented by a single switch in an on or an off position. An electric light with its switch has been compared to a simple computer. The light switch can be either on or off and the light bulb tells you in which position the switch is: either on or off.

In the computer, too, switches or transistors respond to the presence or absence of electric current, and this presence or absence is controlled by switches. The central processor in a computer is a place where calculations are performed by literally thousands of transistor switches continually changing their on-off position.

A system that is only on or off is known as a binary system, one that has just two positions. You may be familiar with binary arithmetic, a system in which only two numbers are used, a 1 and a 0. A computer carries out calculations in binary

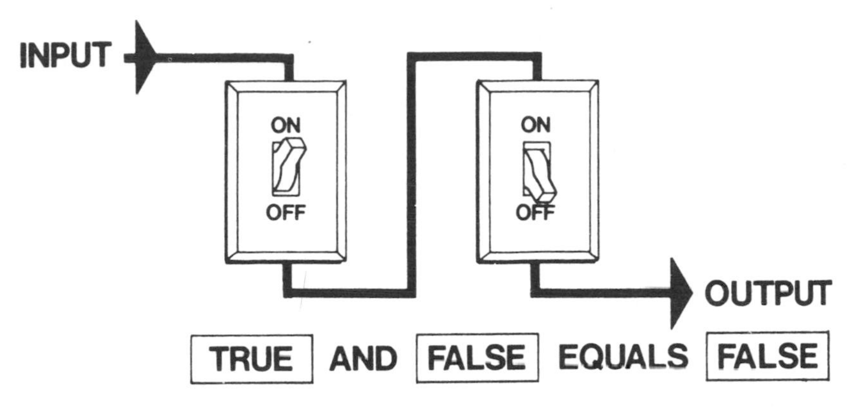

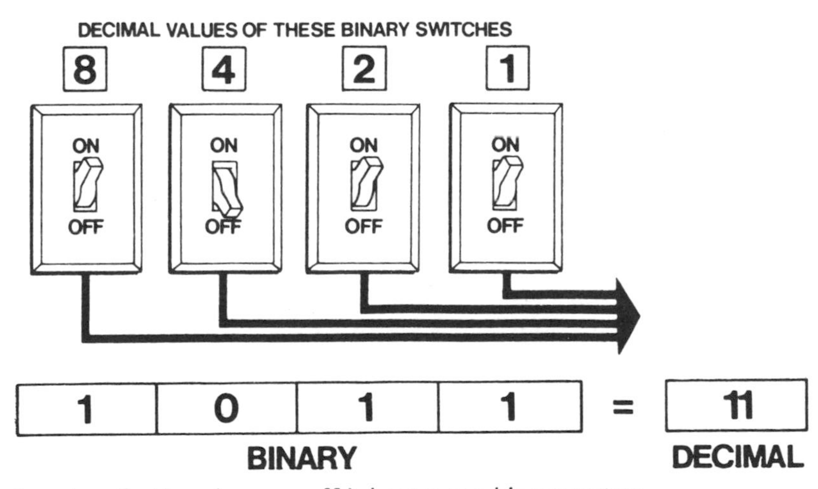

A system that is only on or off is known as a binary system.

—Courtesy of IBM

arithmetic. Switches are either on or off; a switch that is off can represent a 0. A row of switches that can turn off and on can represent a row of numbers based upon the binary representation of 1 or 0.

In computers, millions of individual operations can be carried out in one second, with this binary system as the basic building block. A binary digit is commonly called a bit and a sequence of adjacent binary digits, or bits, operated as a unit are called bytes. A byte is a basic unit of information stored in the computer and usually consists of eight bits.

Patterns of 1's and 0's can be used to represent more than numbers. Computers can represent one kind of thing in terms of another by allowing the numbers to represent letters, shades of color, speeds, weights, and an almost endless list of things. You are probably familiar with the Morse code that is used to represent letters. Computers codes are a much more flexible form of handling information than the "da dit" system.

More than a century ago, George Boole, the mathematician, worked out a system of algebra that is based on symbols which can be binary in character. Part of this mathematical language consists of elements that are either true or false and, as such, the algebra is logical in structure rather than arithmetic. Since the binary digits, 0 and 1, can stand for false and true respectively, a computer can be used to solve logical as well as numerical problems. This two-valued logic fits in beautifully with the way computers operate.

Another major contribution to the world of computers was made long ago by another mathematician, Charles Babbage. In fact, Babbage is often considered to have invented the computer. His strange looking "analytical engine" (although never completed) was the beginning of programmable computers. It had a set of input devices or methods by which he could

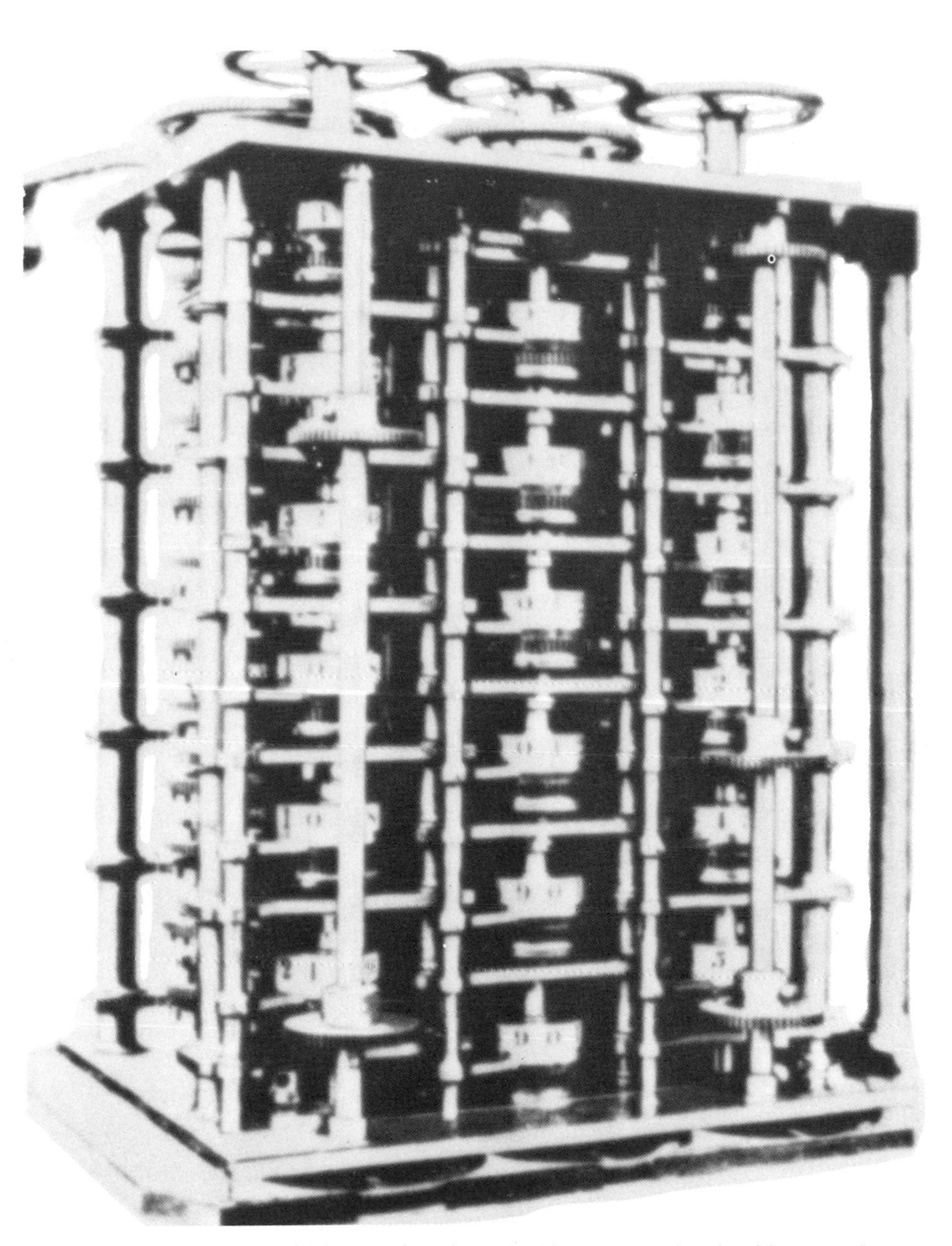

The "Babbage" calculator played a significant part in the history of today's complex computers. *–Courtesy of IBM*

feed numbers or instructions into it. It had an arithmetic unit or processor where the numbers were calculated, a control unit where certain tasks were completed in proper sequence, a memory where numbers could be stored waiting their turn to be processed, and an output mechanism. These are the five basic components of any computer.

The many columns of toothed wheels and the many rods that clanked in the Babbage machine were quite different from a modern computer, but this and other calculators played a significant part in the history of today's complex machines.

One characteristic runs through the development of computers as well as the popular simple computers that just handle numerical calculations, the hand calculators. That characteristic is increased speed and efficiency, achieved with a reduction in size. From the abacus, a manual device that is still used in some countries, to modern data processing machines, efficiency and speed are important. Today's computers are systems of machines the speeds of which are measured in microseconds (millionths of a second) or nanoseconds (billionths of a second). The human mind cannot imagine such speeds, but it may help to compare what a computer can do in the half second that it takes spilled coffee to reach the floor.

Within the time it takes coffee spilled from a pot on the table to reach the floor, a fairly large computer can debit 4200 checks to 630 bank accounts, *and* examine the electrocardiograms of 210 patients and alert physicians in case of trouble, *and* score 315,000 answers on 6300 examinations, evaluating the effectiveness of the questions, *and* figure the payroll for a company with over 2,000 employees, *plus* more chores.*

**Calculations courtesy C. D. Siegchrist, IBM Technical Editor.*

Early computers were large and slow.

—Courtesy of IBM

An old card sorter cost more than many of today's multi-purpose machines.

—Courtesy of IBM

The following experiment also may help you to have some understanding of the speed at which computers function. Time yourself as you multiply 3548 by 754. Did it take you a minute or so? How long does it take you to do this multiplication on a pocket calculator? How did you spend most of the time with

This electronic multiplier dates to 1946. —*Courtesy of IBM*

---

the calculator? Which answer do you think has a greater chance of being accurate, the handwritten one or the one from the calculator? If you could eliminate the time it took to turn on the calculator, push the buttons, and read the answer, you would reduce the time for this procedure so much that the remaining time used for the actual multiplication process is very small indeed. The very fact that computers can operate so accurately with what seems like instantaneous speed has been suggested as one reason so many people feel uncomfortable about these machines.

There is another trend in the history of computers. This is reduction in size. Long ago, the most complicated computers were called "giant brains," a name that may have had an influence on the people who resist the idea of artificial intelligence. In any case, the so-called giant brains really were very large computers. These computers were not only massive, they were comparatively slow.

Mark I, which was considered to be the world's first operational electromechanical computer, was unveiled in 1944 after five years of work by Harvard's Dr. Howard Aiken, with the help of IBM. It stood over eight feet tall and weighed five tons. In its 51 feet of length, it contained over 500 miles of wiring and almost a million different components. This machine could multiply two 23 digit numbers in six seconds.

I. J. Good and D. Michie were among the pioneers who developed the computer in England that many people believe "won the war" for the Allies because of its ability to crack the German codes. This computer, the Colossus, used 200 radio-type tubes, an almost unbelievably large number for the time. These could flip on and off like switches and could count thousands of times faster than could moving mechanical parts. The Colossus and the electronic computers that soon followed it were developed only to crack enemy codes.

An all-purpose computer that was built at the University of Pennsylvania and installed at the Aberdeen weapons proving ground in Maryland in 1947 contained 19,000 tubes, was as large as a six-room house, weighed 28 tons, and needed as much electricity as a small power station to operate it. Called ENIAC (Electronic Numeral Integrator and Calculator), this computer had to be rewired each time a new program was used. Soon after this, the world-famous mathematician John von Neumann introduced the concept of internally stored programs, an important step in the development of computers.

Many smaller, more efficient computers followed. By 1946, IBM vacuum-tube machines could multiply two 10 digit numbers in 1/40th of a second. By 1953 it took only 1/2000th of a second.

The new age of computers came with a revolutionary invention at the Bell Telephone Laboratories in 1947: the transistor. While in a vacuum tube electrons move through the open space that has been evacuated, in transistors, the electrons move through a solid crystal. This makes possible a great reduction in size and in the amount of energy needed to power the systems using them. Most transistors are made of silicon. Today the silicon chip is a well-known term.

The specially prepared silicon used is a semi-conductor, a material that will not conduct an electric current until the current rises to a certain level. When it reaches this point, the electricity suddenly flows through the silicon and the switch is on. This makes it an excellent material for computers.

Transistors can easily be connected to function in an on/off arrangement on silicon chips. With modern technology, the number of transistors on a chip has increased tremendously and the capacity of computers has increased along with this. Since computers are basically nothing more than a vast collection of electrical switches that turn off and on, a computer can be made to handle more information per second by increasing the number of switches. The more circuits, the more a computer can do.

In 1960, one transistor fit on a silicon chip. That is, the chip was the transistor. Its size was a square just about a half

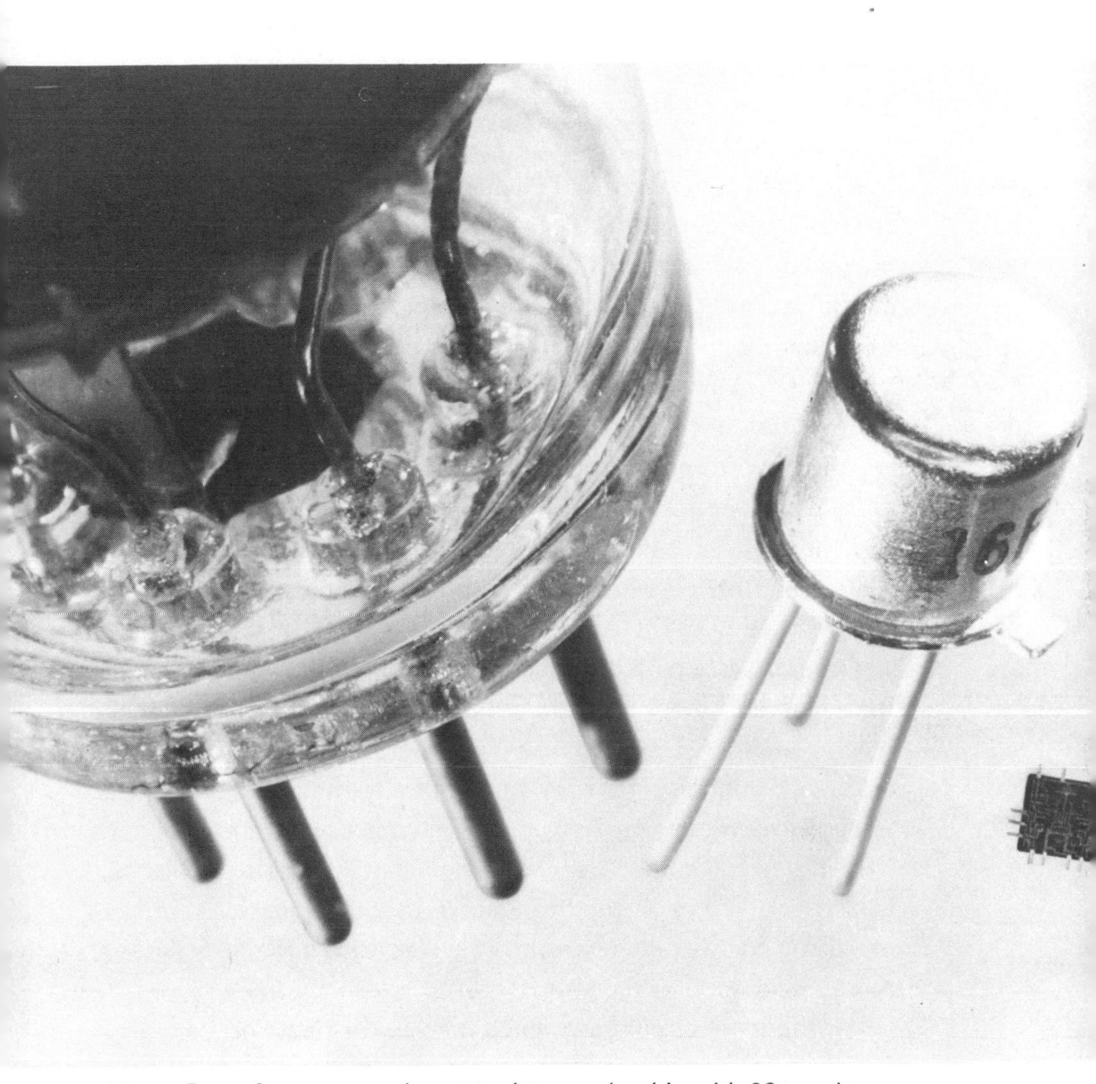

Above: Part of a vacuum tube, a transistor, and a chip with 22 transistors.
Bell Telephone Laboratories

Opposite: A primitive transistor, 1947. *Bell Telephone Laboratories*

centimeter on each side. Ten years later, a thousand transistors could be squeezed into this tiny space. By 1980 a hundred thousand switching units could be squeezed onto a single chip, making one tiny piece of silicon more powerful than some of the early computers. Today's researchers are working toward a million circuits on a chip. While the quest for miniaturization continues, computers play an increasingly larger role in the lives of people, whether or not they realize it. From the chemical processing plant that an engineer operates from a remote site with a computer that monitors heat, light, weight, and humidity to the electronic games that entertain people of all ages, computers help to make life easier and more pleasant.

Reduction in the size of switches is one way to increase the capability of a computer. Another way is to make them turn on and off faster. A microprocessor, the computer's arithmetic system, is an electronic circuit on a chip in which the wires and the insulators are all formed together in a single block of silicon. This is known as an integrated circuit, a term used to distinguish it from earlier arrangements in which the transistors were made first and the connections were added by means of wires and solder. A grid of metallic strips on the chip is used to connect the transistors to other parts. A microprocessor connected to a control system and a memory system make a microcomputer.

Producing circuits on chips is a very intricate process since the "wiring" is so fine. Workrooms are surgically clean, for a tiny speck of dust would ruin a chip. A chip one quarter inch on the side may contain over 25 feet of wiring. Using one process, IBM can print the entire Bible, all 1250 pages of the

---

A memory chip in the eye of a needle. *—Courtesy of IBM*

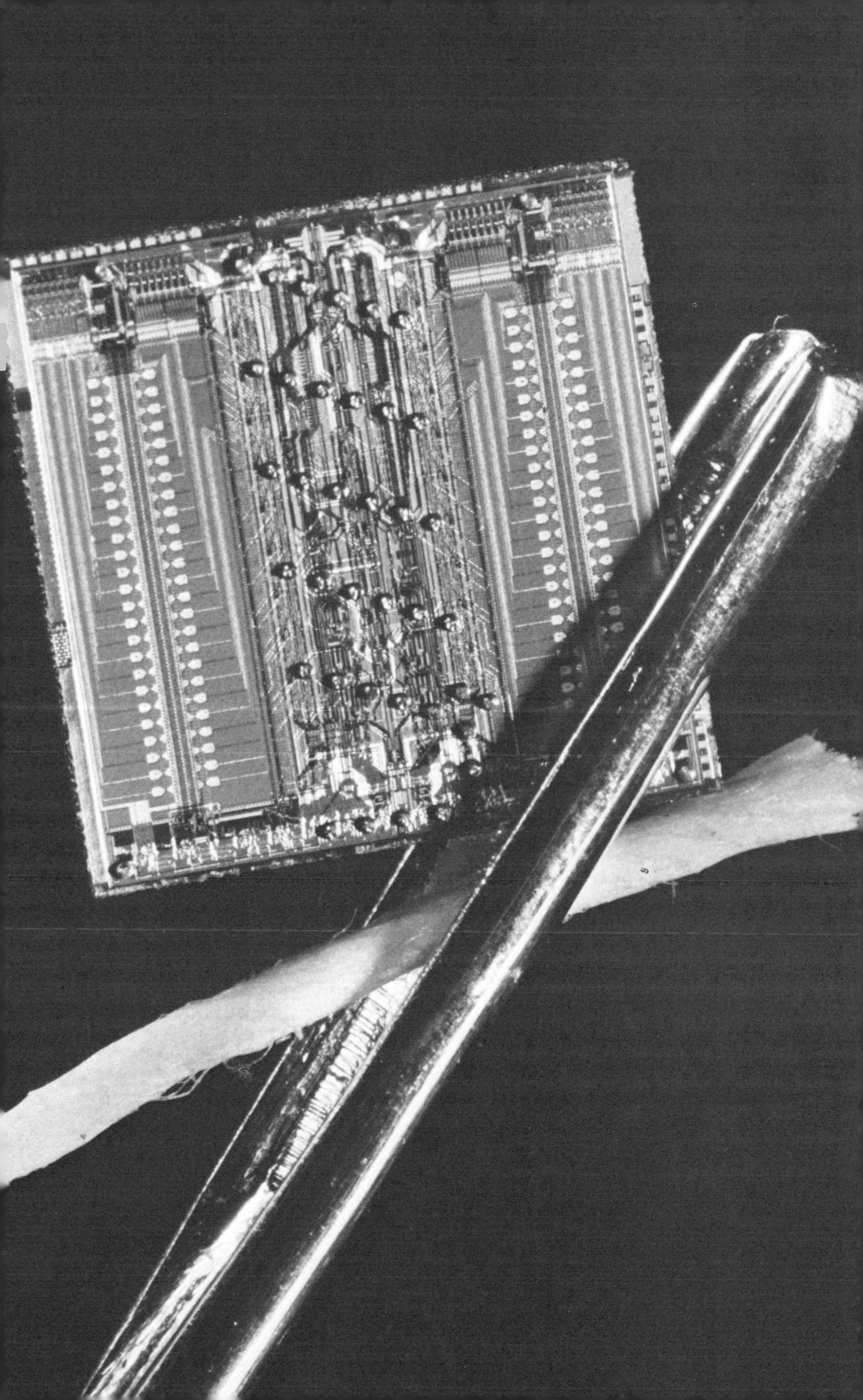

Old and New Testaments, on a wafer 1½ inches square.

Not only can circuits be made unbelievably small, but they can be made to switch on and off at incredible speeds, measured in trillionths of a second. Signals travel through wiring at the rate of slightly less than 12 inches per billionth of a second, or per nanosecond.

Today's computer researchers are trying to make computers even faster so that they will be ever more powerful. Part of this speedup process is achieved by jamming switches even closer together. This reduces the length of wiring between them. New technologies may someday enable the cramming of millions of switches into a space about as small as a grapefruit to make a "supercomputer" that could process 10 to 12 times as much information as the most powerful computers of today. This would be an entirely new species of machine that used technology different from that used in today's computers. Many of today's computers handle 7 to 10 million instructions per second, and some can handle a trillion, but a supercomputer would be capable of handling 70 million to 100 million instructions per second. One can barely guess how such increased capability would affect the search for artificial intelligence.

4.

MOVING TOWARD INTELLIGENT ROBOTS

Fashioning robots that would perform tasks to help people is an ancient dream. Perhaps the very earliest work in the search for artificial intelligence was the creation of mythical robots.

Although many people think of Frankenstein's monster when they picture a robot, the original in Mary Shelley's story was created before the word "robot" came into use. Many derivations of the original story have kept it alive.

A very popular story that is much older than Frankenstein is the story of Golem, a robot-like creature made of clay. According to one version of this story, the chief rabbi of Prague created a creature in the year 1580 from clay of the local riverbank. He named it Joseph Golem and he made it for the purpose of spying on the enemies of the Jews. The rabbi, with the help of two assistants, formed it in the dead of night and, after proper incantations and prayers, implanted the name of God on the creature's forehead. It came alive!

Although Joseph Golem could not talk, the rabbi managed to make good use of it as a spy. When the robot was not busy with that task, it served as the rabbi's janitor. One day, the rabbi's wife asked Joseph Golem to bring water from the well without being specific about how much water. The creature brought more and more water until the rabbi was called from his devotions to bring the situation under control. There were many times when the "golem" was troublesome and at times, *it* appeared to be in control. This idea of losing control to robots is one that motivates some of the people who oppose research in the field of artificial intelligence. The rabbi was able to destroy the Joseph Golem, perhaps by removing the name of God from its forehead. However, the idea of a golem continued to be used in various stories, and in medieval Jewish legend, a golem was any automaton-like clay servant that was brought to life by means of a charm.

Mechanical dolls and other creatures that worked by mechanical means became popular in later years, and many of these were the subjects of stories in which they were made and destroyed by a variety of means. The stories of Pinnochio, the Emperor's Nightingale, Dorothy's adventures with the scarecrow and the tin woodman in the Land of Oz, Alice and the playing cards that came to life at the mad queen's party, the toy soldiers that marched at midnight in the Nutcracker Suite, and the Frankenstein monster continue to entertain people.

The word "robot" did not come into popular use until the early 1920's with the appearance of a play called R.U.R. (Rossum's Universal Robots) in which artificial zombie-like creatures took over the world. Although there are many definitions of robots today, they are generally described as creatures, or machines, that function under their own power and control.

This robot was built by Dr. Michael Freeman when he was 13 years old. His teaching robot, 2 XL, is popular with children.

—Courtesy of Dr. Michael Freeman

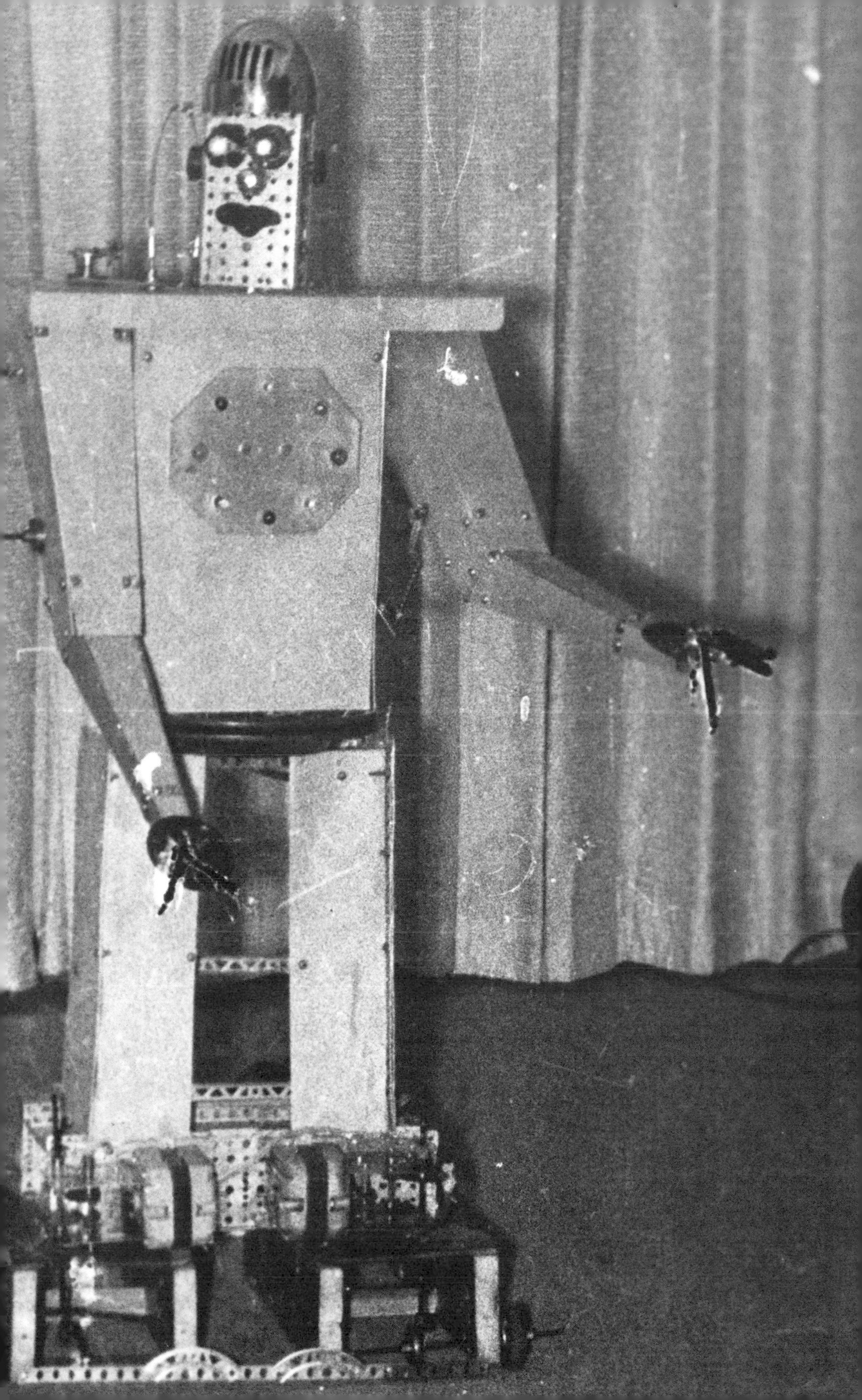

Robots in science fiction are ever popular, even though they are quite different from the robots that work for humans in the real world. In the past, many fictional robots were unpleasant or evil characters that gained control of humans, and it was common for people to think of these artificial creatures as dangerous. The robots of space fiction have done much to change the current feelings about robots, for they usually follow the three famous "Laws of Robotics." These were suggested back in the year 1950 by the author Isaac Asimov:

1. A robot may not harm a human being or allow a human being to come to harm through inactivity of the robot.
2. A robot must obey the orders or commands given to it by human beings unless these conflict with the first law.
3. A robot must protect itself at all times as long as such protection does not conflict with the first two laws.

The popular robots in the film *Star Wars* and many other fictional robots are law-abiding creatures. They are often very appealing in appearance and personality. Certainly they are much different from most of the actual robots that work in industry and are being developed in the laboratories of artificial intelligence researchers.

Some of the actual robots of earlier times were appealing, too. In the eighteenth century, mechanical figures of animals and humans were especially popular. These performed a series of actions that imitated real life. A model of a person dipped pen in ink and wrote on a pad. A flute player, the size of a human, played 12 melodies. Mechanical people danced and mechanical ducks drank and splashed in the water. They all followed specific programs of actions that were determined by a device similar to the mechanism contained in music boxes. This type of robot is sometimes called a "clockwork automaton."

In the modern world mechanical figures do not seem threatening, but in the eighteenth century they inspired discussions about whether or not machines can think. Many people found them disturbing, just as many people today are disturbed by the search for artificial intelligence. In the eighteenth century, some mechanical figures were accused of being the work of witches, and at least one designer of automatic people was arrested on the charge of witchcraft by the Holy Inquisition.

Many years later, in 1948, the British brain physiologist W. Grey Walter invented an appealing type of robot he called a "machina speculatrix," but which was popularly known as a tortoise or turtle. There were many of these turtles, but each was a metal box on wheels in which there were two "sense organs." One "sense organ" was a bank of photocells that looked in the direction in which the tortoise was steering. In the absence of light, the turtle kept going around in circles, but when a light shown on it, it moved toward the light. However, if the light were very bright, the turtle moved away from it.

The other "sense organ" in the mechanical turtles was the shell, or box that housed the internal equipment, which, since it looked somewhat like a turtle, was responsible for giving them this popular name. If a turtle bumped into something, the shell detected this and the turtle moved along a random path until it cleared the obstacle.

One of the most interesting behaviors of the original turtle and its many "children" was the way these mechanical creatures returned to their "hutches" when their batteries needed recharging. Grey Walter placed battery chargers in the corners of the room, where the turtles could connect themselves when the batteries were low. Here they could plug in and "feed."

The Terrapin Turtle, designed by Dan Hillis of MIT's Artificial Intelligence Laboratory, is used in schools and laboratories throughout the world.

—Courtesy of Terrapin, Inc.

One of the purposes for building the turtles was to study the electrical activity of the brain. They also served the purpose of making people question whether or not they were "beings," since they had senses that could detect a stimulus and respond to it. They spawned numerous offspring, including the computer turtles that have been used in some recent teaching situations.

A robot turtle, the Terrapin Turtle, designed by Dan Hillis of Massachusetts Institute of Technology's Artificial Intelligence Laboratory, is being used by schools, colleges, universities, and research laboratories around the world. It is a computer-controlled device that has blinking eyes, beeps in two tones, draws with a pen, and moves on two separately controlled wheels. Most important, the Terrapin Turtle has a sense of touch. It provides a wide variety of learning opportunities as well as recreation.

Modern teaching robots take many forms, and some of the more exciting and smarter robots will be discussed in another chapter.

While scientists are searching for ways to make robots more intelligent, many dumb, low-level robots have been invading industry. For some processes, the machines do not have to be very sophisticated, but they appear intelligent compared with mechanical figures of former times. Consider the robots that work at the Roundtree Chocolate factory in England. They have two arms which give them the ability to pick up two pieces of candy at a time and place them in boxes. The most amazing thing about them is their speed. These robots work at the rate of two pieces of candy every second. The robots work tirelessly, never stopping for a coffee break. No worker ever stayed on this job in the chocolate factory for more than two years. The new workers never get bored, nor are they ever absent because of illness, vacation, or lack of transportation.

The Terrapin Turtle moves on two separately controlled wheels and has a sense of touch. *—Courtesy of Terrapin, Inc.*

Robot mailmen are often speedier than the office mailmen, who stop to chat with people when they make their rounds. To some of the people who watch them, the robots seem rather bright. Suppose you are walking down the hall in an office building and a robotic mail cart comes along the hall on its way to delivering and collecting mail at your office and the others on your floor. You decide to see what happens if you stand in its way. The robot hits you with a gentle bump and waits until you step aside. You continue on your way and the robot continues on its way. This is just what it was programmed to do in case of such an emergency. In some ways it does not seem at all stupid, even though its computer "brain" is rather simple. It must only control a few functions, such as stop, start, turn, and beep horn. "Blue Eyes," a government-employed mail cart, has two twinkling lights on in front when it is operating, and like many other computer controlled carts, is a popular member of the office staff.

Many industrial robots do their jobs more efficiently and produce better results than people did in the same kind of work. Thousands of them are working in jobs that are hard, dangerous, or just boring. They don't mind working in places that are hot, freezing cold, dusty, or dangerous. They don't ask for overtime or care how long they work. Their "up time" is about 95% compared with that of human workers at 75%.

The industrial robot pictured on page 61 welds a base assembly that will hold computer parts. The robot welds 44 two-inch seams from a variety of angles in less than 12 minutes. It took 45 minutes for a human to weld this same kind of assembly.

Robots weld, load, and unload hot and heavy metal forms into machines that stamp them into a variety of shapes. And they do their jobs well. Robot car painters do a better job than

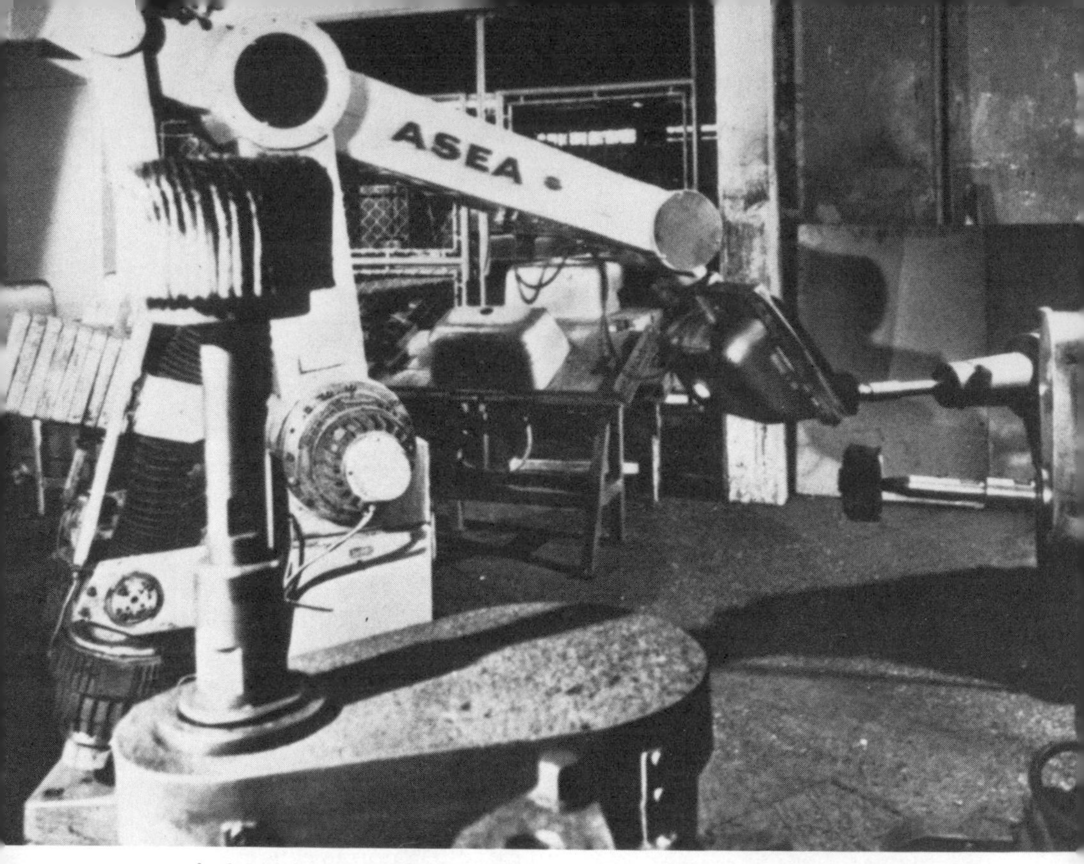

Industrial robots perform tasks that are hard, dangerous, or just boring for the ordinary person. This robot is polishing sinks. *—Courtesy of ASEA*

people. General Motors expects to be using 1500 robot painters by the year 1990.

You might find it rather awesome to watch a robot at work. Its arm moves through the welding operation with a certain amount of grace, imitating the human arm and hand with a wide radial motion that seems too effortless and powerful. But even the most sophisticated robot hands cannot approach the complexity of the human kind.

The robot that replaces about a dozen workers at the Chesebrough-Pond's thermometer plant protects people from the possibility of mercury poisoning. Working in an isolated room, its computer brain guides it through a seven and one-half minute, 394-step program in which it works with two dozen different boxes. The robot follows a simple routine of

This robot welds 44 two-inch seams in less than 12 minutes—almost a quarter of the time it would take a human being to weld the same assembly.

—Courtesy of Cincinnati Milacron

lowering a box full of thermometers into a tank of hot water, transferring them into a tank of cold water, and placing them in a centrifuge. The purpose of all this is to squeeze out any air bubbles that might be present in the mercury that measures temperature. These would interfere with the accuracy of the thermometers.

Many factory workers who have been replaced by robots consider them helpers and are glad to let the robots do the unpleasant and dangerous jobs. Welding cars and spraying paint are ideally done at temperatures hotter than a human can stand.

The picture on the opposite page shows one of a variety of things that robots do today. Robots can spot weld auto bodies in eight places at once. They can lift and transfer 50-pound loads three times as fast as men. But they are still stupid machines. They need not be a threat so long as workers replaced are put into better or more interesting jobs. Even though the robots are vulnerable to sabotage, there have been no workers who have exhibited violence of the kind demonstrated by the followers of Edward Ludd, who physically attacked early machines of the industrial revolution. Luddites, as they were called, were concerned both for the workers who were being displaced by machines, and upset about the new technology. Technical innovations have long been feared and hated.

Many workers today are fond of the robots that help in industry, on farms, and in health care. Some of the robots are given names by their human co-workers and when "Clyde the Claw" broke down at an automobile stamping plant, it was given a get-well party. There are questions about how long this attitude will continue as the robot revolution, now in its infancy, moves ahead at a rapid pace. In the automobile industry, for example, robots are taking on an increasingly large number of jobs. Before long, about 800 robots at General Motors

Some industrial robots can weld auto bodies in eight places at once.
–Courtesy of ASEA

Corporation will weld the bodies of just about every new car that comes from the assembly line.

In the autombile industry more and more robots are

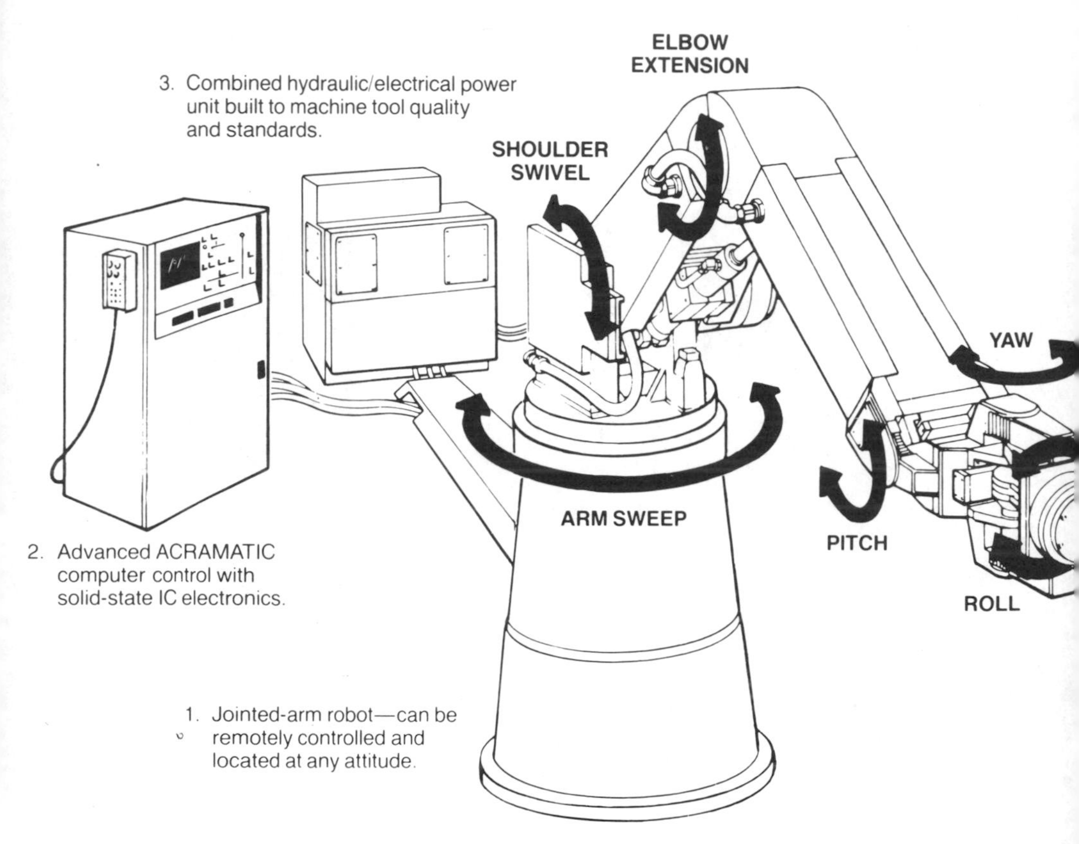

This diagram of an industrial robot clearly shows the parts that add to its agility and versatility. *–Courtesy of Cincinnati Milacron*

---

expected to do work that surpasses that which can be done by humans. For example, on an assembly line there are slight variations due to the human element as an automobile body moves from one step to another. This can mean missed welds, poorly fitting doors, rattles, and leaks. Robots work exactly the same way each time. In some automobile plants, robots will be used to stamp steel panels into complete automobile bodies. An entire automobile body can be assembled in two or three steps with the help of a computerized robot system.

Robots can work on small objects, too, and in many processes that do not fit into assembly-line production methods. Consider the versatility of a robot that can write its name on the blackboard, then erase it, then write again. One continued this pattern for hours on end at a recent robotics show, but it was just a dumb robot.

Teaching these robots to work is the responsiblity of humans. There are three typical ways of programming these so-called "first generation" or low-level robots. "Lead through" is a method in which the operator guides the robot through the orientation and locations that are desired by means of a remote control "teach box" and imprints a pattern on its computer memory. "Walk through" is a method by which the robot is physically guided through the desired motions by a person. These are recorded and played back to the robot. The third method is known as "plug in." Here the robot operates through the use of a prerecorded program without the use of manipulation. "Plug in" programming is faster and a whole library of programs can be stored for future use. However, more problems arise when this method is used because of slight variations.

First-generation robots can do a variety of jobs, not just a repetition of one job as did the early robots that capped bottles. Since they can be programmed to work in different ways, they seem more intelligent than the "push and put" kind of machine—but they are still not very high on the brightness scale when measured against "second generation" robots.

The world's first robot system used to check car body integrity.

—Courtesy of ASEA

Here is an example of a low-level robot making a mess of its job: It is working away performing a sequence of movements that result in the welding of identical pieces of metal. Another pair of pieces is presented to the robot, but this time they are in different positions from the usual ones. The robot is not bright enough to notice this, so it proceeds to weld them, putting the welds in the wrong place.

One of the applications of the search for artificial intelligence is to make smarter robots.

5.

COMPUTERS WITH VISION

A surface-roving vehicle lands on the moon and navigates a narrow path between two craters, independent of human control. Its computer brain has been programmed to send information back to earth and its computer-instructed sense organs help the robot to find its path. Suddenly, a moonquake changes the surface, and the robot slides down the side of a crater. It is intact but disoriented until it "looks around." The robot's vision enables it to compare the present location with the path above by examining the patterns of features such as boulders, mountains, and the sides of the crater. The robot compares this scene with the description of surroundings made shortly before it fell. It climbs up the crater wall to its original position and scoops up some sand in its mechanical hand. This is not the description of a robot in science fiction or one planned for 20 years from now, but of one that might be at work soon.

Robots with vision are already at work. At Texas Instruments Corporation, for example, camera-assisted robots inspect glowing diodes that are to light the numbers in pocket

This Mars surface robot may operate for two years and travel about 1000 km performing experiments automatically and sending information back to earth. *—Jet Propulsion Laboratory*

calculators. Humans could do this kind of inspection for only about two hours before all the lights would look alike to them. Robot "eyes" don't get tired and they do their work well.

As early as 1980, six robots—three sighted and three blind—went to work without the help of a human to assemble a motor that had as many as 50 parts. Of course, humans had done the programming of the robot beforehand.

Although no one expects many robots to walk dogs or do housework in the near future, there are many new and exciting possibilities for robots that can see or use some kind of sensing device. Researchers long have been working toward smarter robots. They know that if a robot is going to be smarter than a simple manipulator, it must be able to respond to its environment. In addition to having arms that are jointed, claws that work like fingers, and computer brains, it needs to "see," "touch," or detect things in some other way.

Picture a robot arm reaching into a bin for a part that is needed for the next step in assembling a motor. The bin is full of different kinds of parts. How will the robot know which part to choose?

Television cameras that are positioned near the robot feed information to its computer brain, which has memorized the images of objects that the robot is processing. When the correct object is recognized, the computer calculates its distance and orientation and moves the robot's arm so that it will grip the right piece. This is a second generation robot, a robot with vision that can respond to its environment.

Robots that respond to the environment are the result of many laboratory experiments through a number of years. One experimental robot that is particularly appealing is known as The Beast, a robot that was built by scientists at the Johns Hopkins University Applied Physics Laboratory. Its real name was Adaptive Mobile Automaton. However, this name was changed to "The Beast" by newsmen and the robot was soon affectionately called that by the scientists who worked with it. The Beast was shaped like an oversized hatbox with a retractable head. Sensors enabled it to feel its way along the wall. When the Beast reached one of the four electrical outlets available to it, the head would position itself and two prongs would lock into The Beast's socket. In this way the machine could "feed" itself until the batteries were recharged. During one day of wandering in the hallway, the machine would plug into the outlets about 25 times.

The Beast could avoid tripping over electrical cables or other objects in its path through the use of a stored program in its "brain," and it could avoid falling down the stairs the same way. However, in spite of this robot's ability to adapt, it was never considered to be more than a very dumb robot.

One popular robot that was built in connection with early research in the field of artificial intelligence was called Shakey. While The Beast showed a limited amount of ability to modify its actions in response to conditions that existed in its environment, Shakey was more sophisticated. Shakey was another robot for whom its "colleagues" felt great affection. Back in 1969, when Shakey was developed at the Stanford Research Institute, this robot was popular with newsmen, too. Unfortunately, this popularity, as you will see, contributed to its downfall.

Shakey was a robot that spent much of its time in seven rooms of the laboratory, where it could solve a wide range of different problems. The rooms were connected in various ways by eight doors and there were several large boxes that could be

---

This robot, named "Shakey," solves a wide range of different problems while moving among seven laboratory rooms.

—Courtesy of Stanford Research Institute

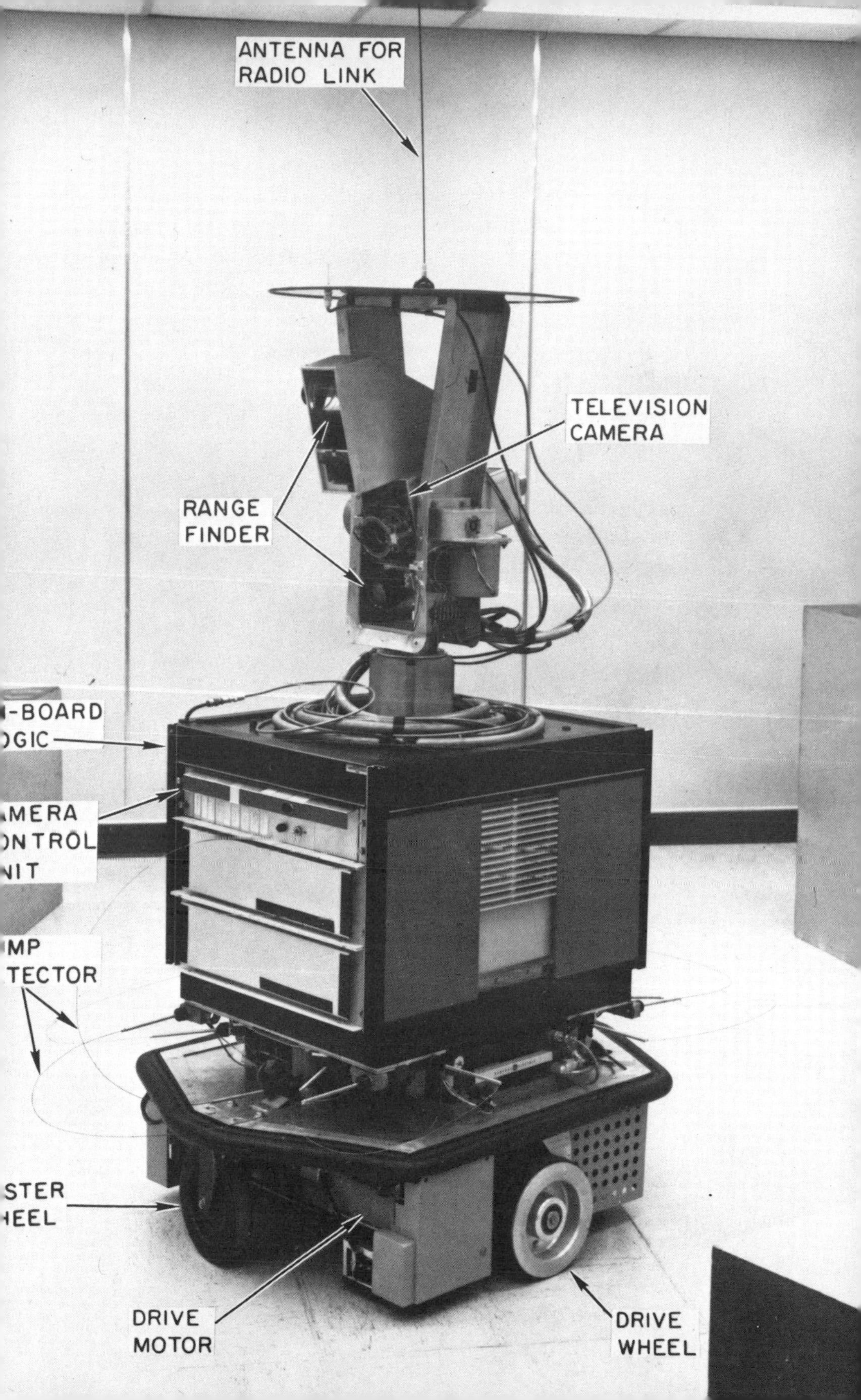

ANTENNA FOR
RADIO LINK

TELEVISION
CAMERA

RANGE
FINDER

-BOARD
OGIC

AMERA
ONTROL
NIT

MP
TECTOR

STER
HEEL

DRIVE
MOTOR

DRIVE
WHEEL

moved around. Shakey could be ordered to push the boxes from one room to another by use of the computer brain that told it what to do through a program that would accomplish the order.

Shakey was an "intelligent" robot in that it could adapt to changed situations. It was built by researchers in artificial intelligence to learn more about problem solving. At one point, the funding for the research was supported by the Department of Defense, reportedly because someone there hoped that a robot could be developed that could be used as a mechanical spy. Pamela McCorduck, in *Machines Who Think,* suggests that this was reminiscent of the original golem.

Research funding for experiments with Shakey was withdrawn later when a number of people began raising questions about whether or not Shakey was a dangerous thing to have. This was thought to be partly the result of some faulty reporting in which a writer picked out the sensational things, enlarged on them, and left others out. But before Shakey "died," scientists learned much that contributed to automation for industry. Among other contributions were those that helped in the development of the first robot that explored Mars. That robot has fondly been called "Son of Shakey."

The first industrial robots with vision that made their way into factories can be compared to people with very bad eyesight. They see the world around them as a series of blurs. Such robots are valuable only for carrying out simple jobs such as picking up some items and putting them down at a certain place.

Robots with better vision have been developed and now gradually are joining older robots in the labor force. Some of these are so efficient that they can distinguish different sizes and species of fish that have been brought up in a fish net and can use their mechanical arms to separate the fish into bins.

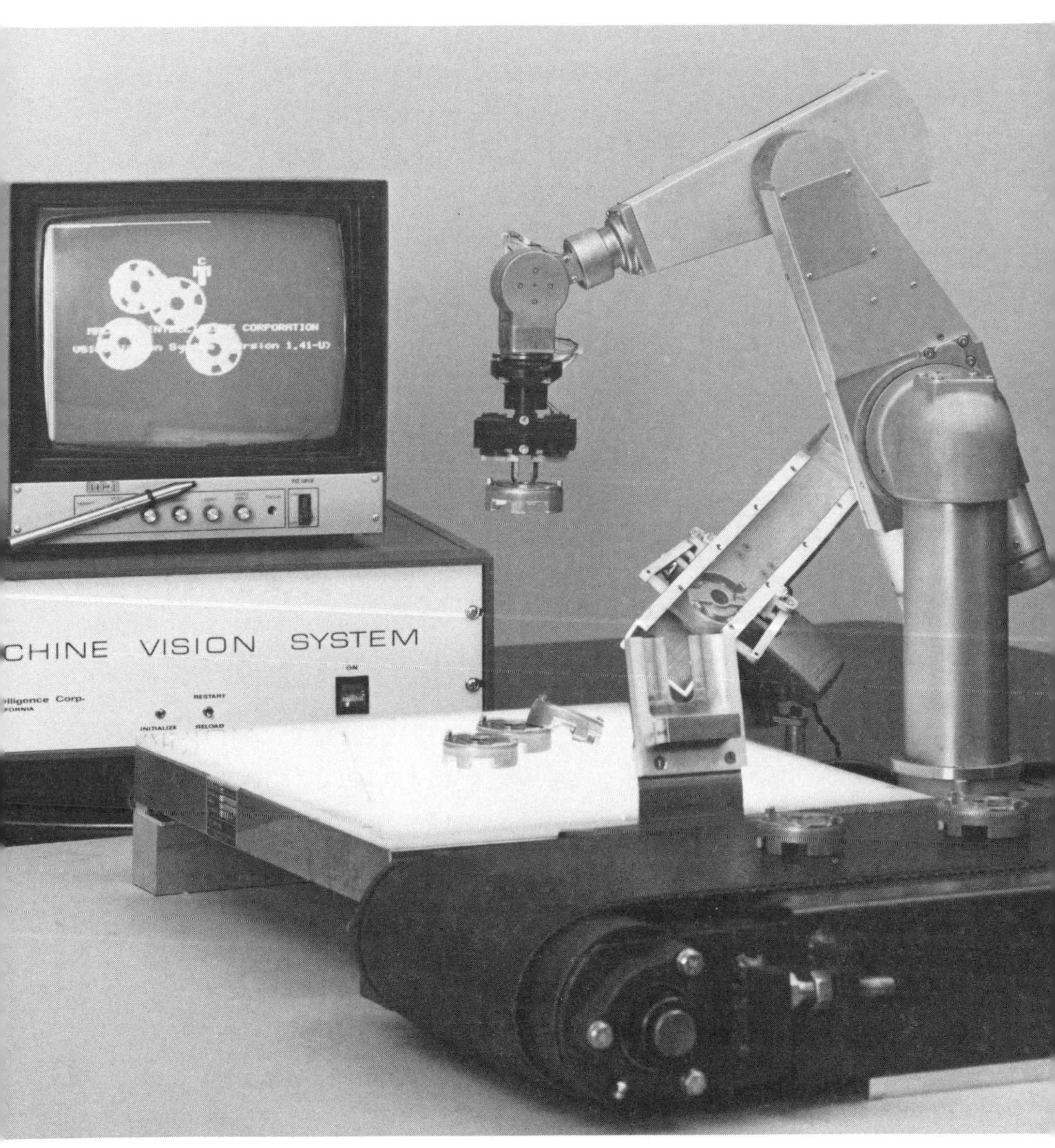

A special robot, combined with a vision system, can measure, identify, and characterize stationary parts. *–Courtesy of Machine Intelligence Corporation*

Some people say such robots sound magical and that they are scary. But the people who train such robots know that they can only see what they have been taught to recognize.

The Univision system is "trained by showing." Pictures of the sample parts that will be seen are made by the camera and records of these are stored in the computer memory. By combining a special robot with a vision system, the machine can measure, identify, and characterize stationary parts. In addition to this, it can do the same for randomly moving parts and make a variety of automatic inspections.

Autovision II, shown on page 77, is another system that may be used to inspect, identify, count, sort, position, and orient parts. It rejects defective parts, too. A random assortment of parts is presented at rates of up to 360 parts per minute, and information about each part is compared with information in the computer's memory to determine whether that part should be used.

The human eye is a highly complex processing system that analyzes what people see and automatically exaggerates some things while ignoring and discarding other things. Machine vision cannot, at this point, be patterned after human vision, but machines can recognize patterns and accomplish some exciting things by different methods.

For example, in robot vision a camera might feed the images that it captures to a computer and these would be converted into code that the computer can recognize. A black and white picture can be divided into squares and a binary number can be assigned to each square representing the shade of grey. You can get some idea of how shades of light and dark can

---

Autovision II is a system used to inspect, identify, count, sort, position, and orient parts. It also rejects defective parts. *—Courtesy of Automatrix, Inc.*

AUTOMATIX
AUTOVISION II

be translated into a series of 1's and 0's for computer use by examining the diagrams on the opposite page.

Think about the scoreboard at a football stadium. Letters and numbers are made by lighting certain bulbs in a grid and keeping some bulbs dark. In computer vision, similarly, each character can be converted into an electronic grid of light and dark spots, and the pattern can be recognized.

Computers have been reading letters and numbers for about 20 years. Consider the wide use of computers that read zip codes in the post office. Perhaps you shop at a store that uses the bar codes on packages at the checkout counter. Some cameras can catch the bar code when a package is in any position. The clerk does not have to find the code on the corn flakes package and place the code in a special position so the machine can read it.

A machine can read a printed or typed number or letter but reading handwriting is more difficult. Have you ever wondered why some address forms instruct you to place letters and numbers in small blocks? The computers that are used for these forms can read block letters and numbers when the letters are the proper size and have sufficient separation.

Imagine trying to make a machine that can feed the patterns made by handwriting into a computer? Some people have difficulty reading their *own* handwriting. Researchers believe that such a machine might be developed within the next ten years. However, machines that read a wide variety of *printing* are here today and are performing some very useful tasks such as are performed by reading machines for the blind, discussed in the next chapter.

You can get some idea of the difficulties involved in computer vision by forming a picture of a scissors in your mind. Now, think about how a scissors looks on a table when

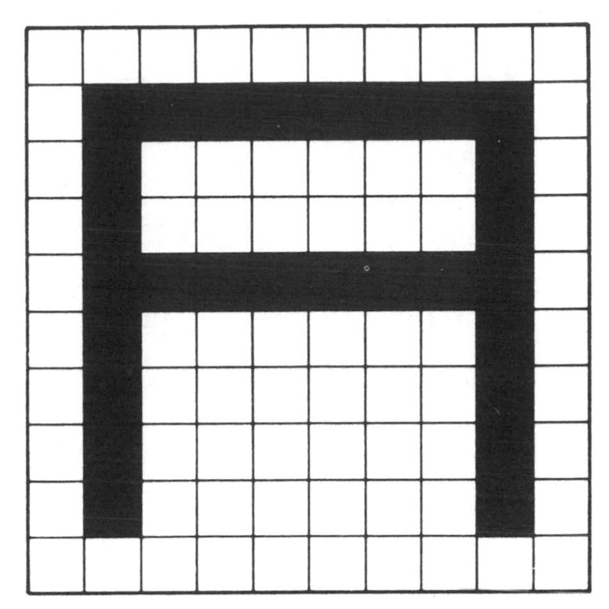

A black and white picture can be divided into squares, and shades of light and dark can be translated into a series of 1's and 0's for computer use.

—Courtesy of Peter Kugel and On Computing magazine

0	0	0	0	0	0	0	0	0	0
0	1	1	1	1	1	1	1	0	0
0	1	0	0	0	0	0	1	0	0
0	1	0	0	0	0	0	1	0	0
0	1	1	1	1	1	1	1	0	0
0	1	0	0	0	0	0	1	0	0
0	1	0	0	0	0	0	1	0	0
0	1	0	0	0	0	0	1	0	0
0	1	0	0	0	0	0	1	0	0
0	0	0	0	0	0	0	0	0	0

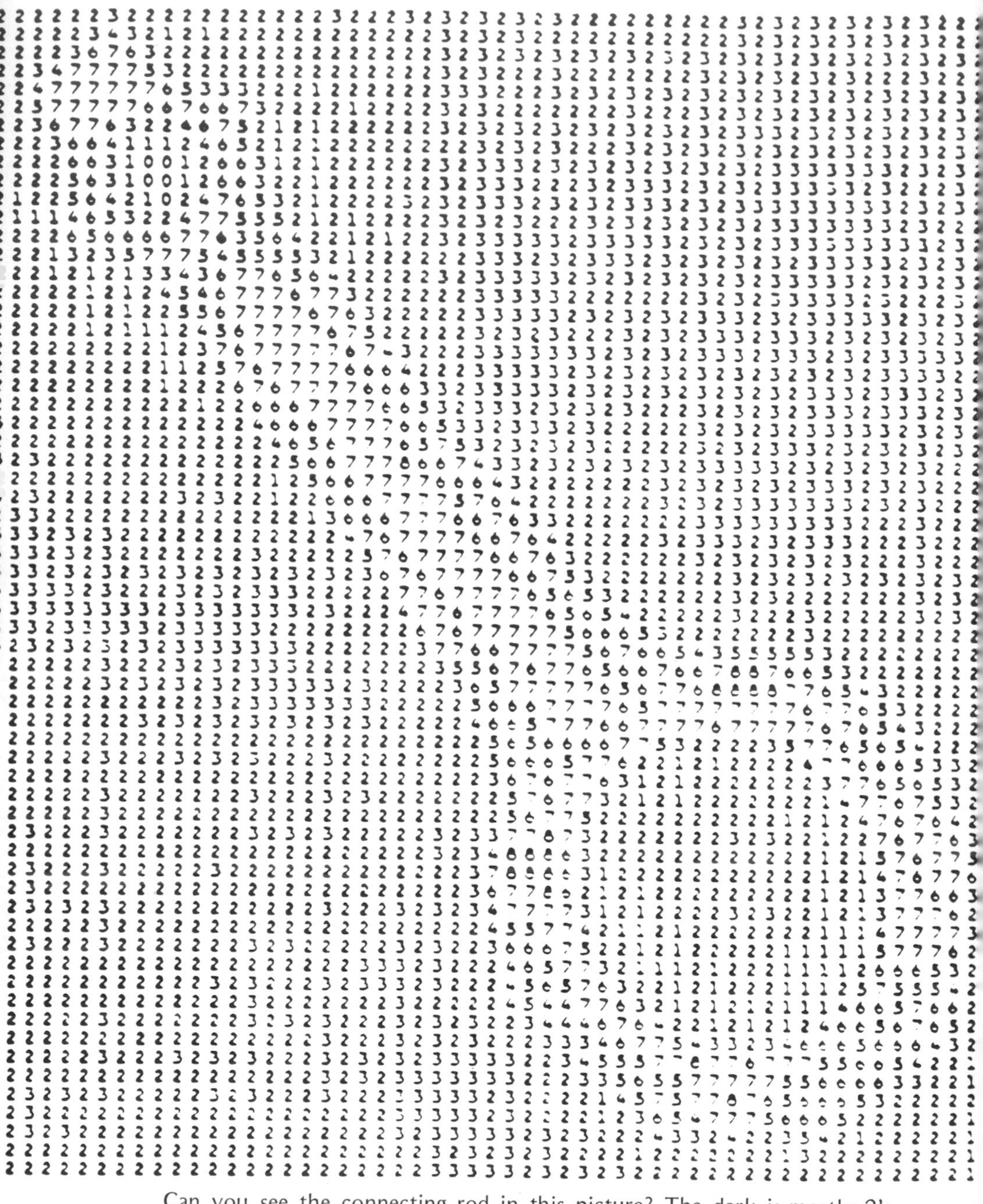

Can you see the connecting rod in this picture? The dark is mostly 2's and 3's while the light connecting rod is mostly 6's and 7's.

–Courtesy of General Motors Research Laboratories

you look at it from above. Suppose you were to stoop so that your eyes were level with the tabletop. How different it would look. But no matter how many ways you look at the scissors, you recognize it. On the other hand, for machine vision, making an object recognizable from all angles is a complex task.

When a computer's camera looks at an object and transmits large numbers of dots to the computer, these are transformed into binary code that depends on the light intensity at each point in the picture. On page 80 is a picture of a connecting rod that has been converted into numbers by a computer at the General Motors Research Laboratories. The range from dark to light has been limited to the numbers 0 to 9, which makes it easier for you.

To make the picture clearer, the digital picture is processed by an "edge finding" computer program. It is not as good as a photograph, but it is clear enough to be recognizable. If a robot can see where a part is, it can pick it up.

The picture on page 83 shows a researcher in a General Motors laboratory experimenting with a seeing robot. The computer translates the picture of a part into a picture it can use (see insert) and instructs the robot to pick it up.

Some artificial intelligence experts believe that eventually a robot will be able to recognize objects it has never seen before by working out the meanings of shapes in much the way a person's brain can reach conclusions about objects he or she has never seen before. The day may not be far away.

Predictions of what robots can do when they have a better sense of touch encourage researchers to imitate the human body, too. Robots with microswitches that close when the hand or arm encounters an object are already in use. And there are strain gauges that measure the force that a robot's hand is exerting on the object it touches.

Suppose a part that is needed for assembling a motor is not

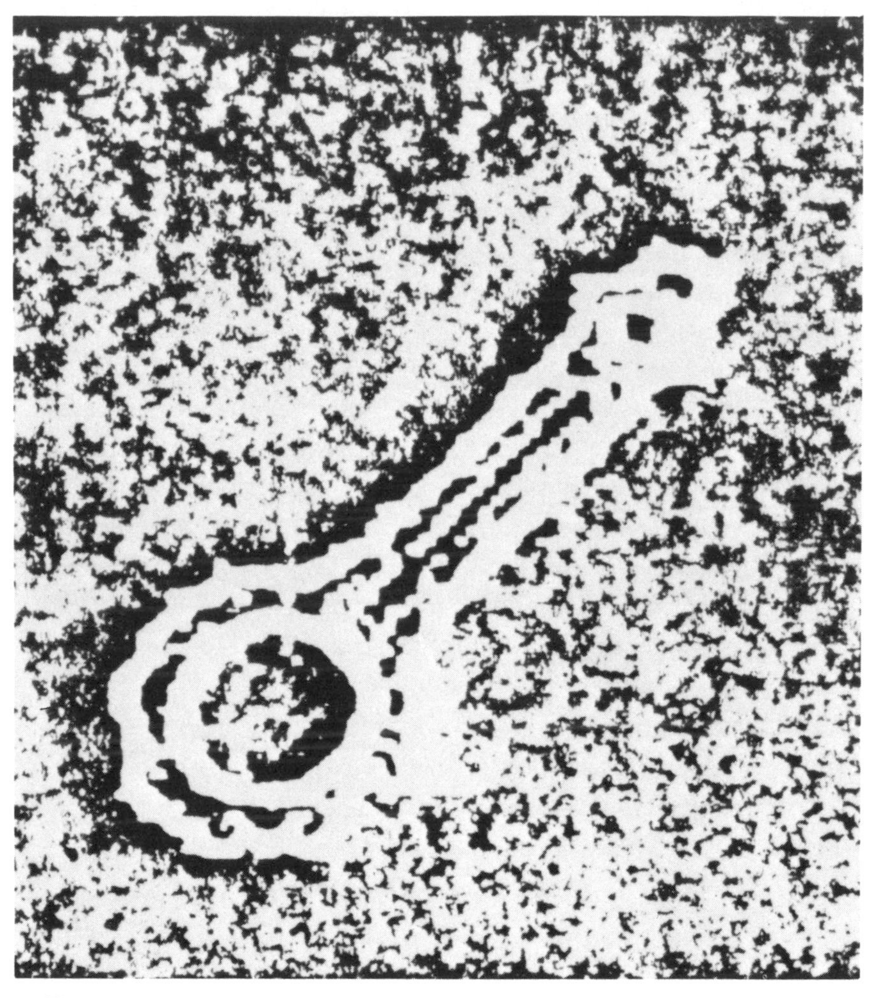

This picture is not as good as a photograph, but it is clear enough for a robot to recognize. *—Courtesy of General Motors Research Laboratories*

A television camera positioned near this robot enables it to locate a part on a conveyor belt. *–Courtesy of General Motors Research Laboratories*

in exactly the right place. A strain gauge could alert the robot's computer, which could send commands to correct the position. A variety of hands that profit from a sense of touch are being explored in laboratories where researchers continue to try to make robots smarter.

Someday, second generation robots that can see and feel may be set loose in large airports, or other places where there are large open spaces, at times when they are not busy. Imagine a large robot vacuum cleaner or polisher moving around without a human to guide it. The computer defines the room's boundaries and guides it to clean everywhere. Optical sensors prevent the machine from bumping into walls and furniture or any person who happens to walk in front of it.

Someday robots may irrigate fields, using exact knowledge of the conditions that exist and the needs of the crops. They also may plow fields, harvest crops and perform a wide variety of other jobs, releasing the farmer for more important duties and allowing more time for recreation. Agriculture is just one of many areas where robots can make life easier for people.

Even today, large numbers of robots that see and feel are beginning to change the way people live. If you visit a library where a machine is reading to a blind person, you may feel that tomorrow already is here.

6.

TALKING, LISTENING, AND UNDERSTANDING STORIES

Teaching computers to read aloud, and do it well, is an extremely complex task, but thanks to artificial intelligence research, hundreds of reading machines are doing just that. Picture a 12-year-old blind boy as he is given a book of his choice. He places a page face down on the Kurzweil Reading Machine at his public library. When he presses a button, the reading machine tells the boy what it sees in a pleasant, slightly accented baritone voice. He listens to page after page until the book is finished, then he chooses another book. Most printed materials are not available in Braille or in Talking Books, so it is no wonder that this boy is spending much of his time at the library. Through the use of sophisticated computers that can read and talk, many new sources of education, entertainment, and culture are available to the blind and those physically handicapped who could not make use of printed materials in the past.

Hundreds of reading machines are helping blind and visually handicapped people between the ages of five and 82. Unfortunately, expense limits the number of machines that are available—but a growing number are being placed in public and

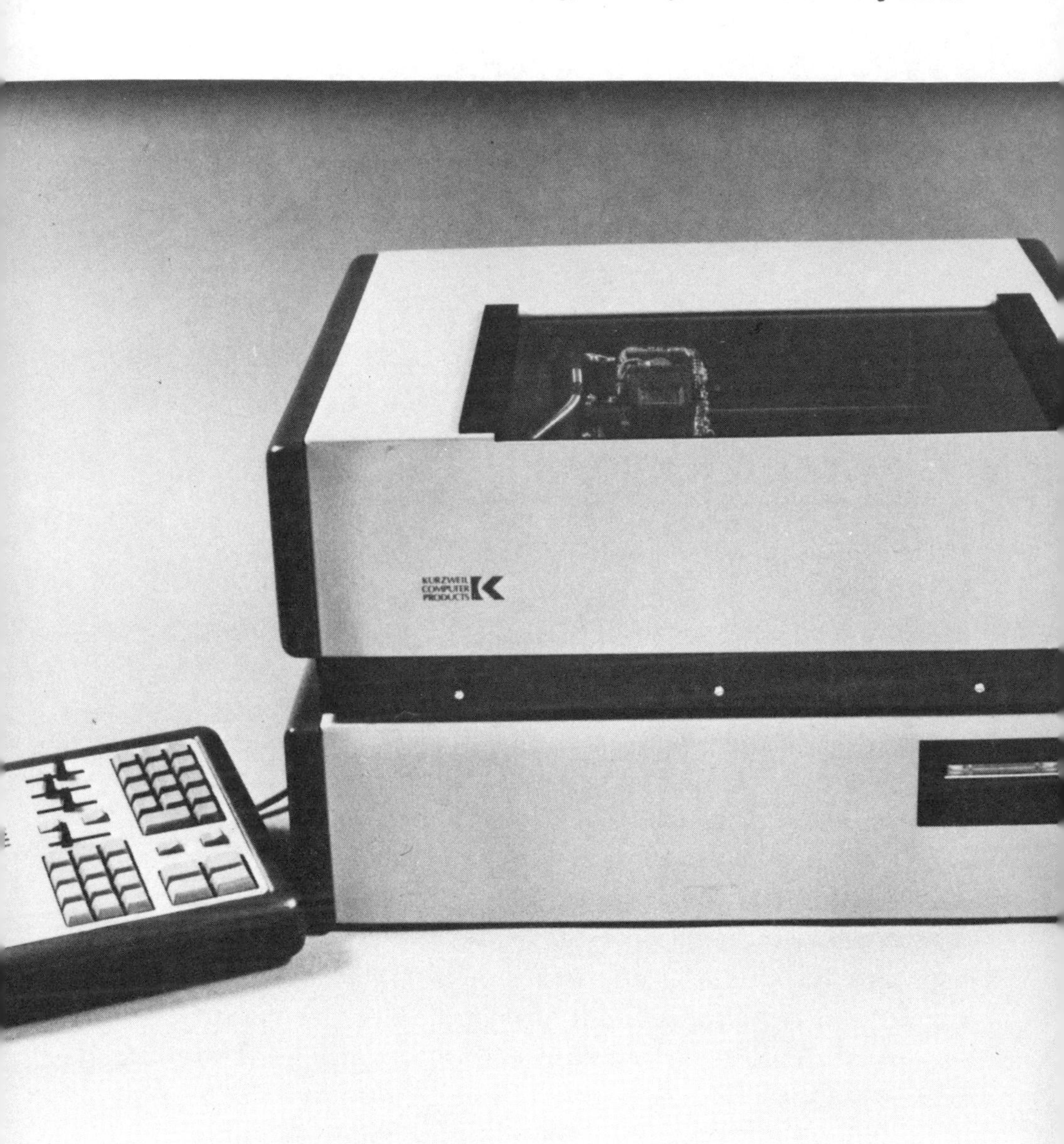

The Kurzweil Reading Machine for the blind consists of three compact units. At the left is the user's keyboard. The scanner, with its glass top on which books or papers are placed, is here shown positioned on the separate computer control unit. *–Courtesy of Kurzweil Computer Products A Xerox Company*

university libraries, schools for the blind, rehabilitation centers, federal and state agencies, and in private corporation libraries.

People who use the reading machines have access to a wide variety of materials because the machine can recognize 300 different varieties of type and can read the print on various colors and qualities of paper. Computers in the machines convert the printed pages into spoken English at a rate as fast as 250 words a minute. This is twice as fast as ordinary human speech. Adjustments can be made for slow readers and fast readers or to produce the speed that any person wants for the kind of material that is being read.

Learning to use the reading machine takes only a few hours. You place the page that is to be read face down on the glass surface of the scanner. Then you activate a separate hand-sized control panel that causes the reading machine to locate the first line of the text automatically. It begins scanning the page, and within a few seconds, an electronic voice can be heard reading the material.

New models of the reading machines allow for voice listening preferences. Controls let users vary the voice that is reading to them by adjusting the itensity of the "s" sounds, voice quality (resonance), and how low or high the pitch is. If you instruct it to do so, the machine will skip ahead in the text or return to an earlier part of the material that you are reading.

Reading machines are not new, but what is new is the way the Kurzweil Reading Machine reads and talks. Some earlier models were slow because the reader had to wait for the computer to search for the word stored in its memory bank. Others could read only a limited number of kinds of type.

The Kurzweil machine uses an advanced form of computer that enables the scanning system to recognize the letters of the

Learning to use the reading machine takes a very short time.

—Courtesy of Kurzweil Computer Products
A Xerox Company

alphabet in almost all printed materials. It uses a system called omni-font optical character recognition, where there is a search for the properties of a letter. For example, the letter "A" may be stored as many different combinations of its features, and these are analyzed to make certain that it is always read as "A." Certain characteristics are common to individual letters even in various types. The letter "A" has a concave area at the base and a loop at the top. The top is a completely closed area of white with extensions at the "west" side and "east" side.

Imagine the difficulty of programming a computer to recognize 300 kinds of type for each letter of the alphabet in both upper and lower case. Making it more complicated is the fact that some letters are poorly printed. The machine can compare a poorly printed letter "A" with well printed "A's" in the same material and recognize the letter for what it is meant to be.

Only after letters are recognized does the machine begin the comparatively simple process of converting the letters, numbers, and words into spoken English. The reading machine records the images that the camera takes from the printed page at the rate of 500 per second. A device on the back of the camera converts each image into electronic signals that the computer translates into characters. It groups these into words and sentences. Now the second part of the process, the talking part, begins. The computer processes pronunciation and articulation, reading with sensitivity to even such fine points as differences in the sound of "d" in the word "red" and the sound of the "d" in the word "reed."

The computer in the reading machine is not just playing back prerecorded words as in the case of many games that "talk." It is synthesizing them from scratch according to 1000 rules and 1500 exceptions to rules that apply to English.

Even though a "talking" computer is extremely complex,

on the whole, it is much easier to design a machine that speaks than it is to design one that listens. Researchers remark that, in this respect, computers are much like humans, for they, too, are better at talking than they are at listening. Scientists have been exploring automatic recognition of natural speech for at least 40 years.

Most listening computers have limited vocabularies, but some of these may soon be useful to wide segments of the population in air traffic reservations and telephone directory assistance where limited vocabularies can be used. Some computers can understand a cross section of American speech, including some foreign accents and regional dialects from North to South and coast to coast. Bell Telephone Laboratories developed a system that builds up the name spoken to it letter-by-letter, from left to right, and checks the stored telephone directory after each addition to make sure that that combination of letters exists. Even though it is accurate, the system obviously is slow.

Progress that has been made in the last few years encourages the idea that a new era in both talking and listening computers may be dawning. For example, IBM research scientists can use a computer to transcribe text from a 1000-word vocabulary. When sentences composed of these words are spoken at a normal pace to the computer, they can be printed automatically with a high degree of accuracy. The United States Air Force is testing a special electronic speech recognition system that has a large vocabulary. If you wish to spend enough money to install the system to activate your appliances by voice command, you can call home and activate a computer that will carry out your instructions to turn on a coffeemaker, a light, a washing machine, or whatever. But the day is far in the future when an efficient, inexpensive

In the future, a robot such as this spacecraft may navigate between Jupiter and its satellites. *—Jet Propulsion Laboratory*

household computer that will obey voice commands is available.

Robots that respond to voice commands are being developed to aid the handicapped. For example, at the Rehabilitative Engineering and Development Center in Palo Alto, California, engineers are developing a "smart arm" that can be attached to a wheel chair or a mobile platform. Among its many abiltities is to respond to a person who tells it to move right or left, flex its elbow, or lift or close its hand.

Although progress is being made in teaching computers how to listen, there is still much to be learned before you can hope to talk to a computer the way the space traveler spoke to Hal in *2001: A Space Odyssey.*

Artificial intelligence researchers have long been working toward the goal of English language understanding as part of their attempts to make computers smarter as well as easier to use. They are aware that many people resist talking to computers by way of artificial languages that computers understand. The machines would seem more friendly if one could ask for information in a natural language rather than having to communicate by means of BASIC, FORTRAN, or any of the other computer languages through the use of a typewriter-like keyboard. There could be more of a feeling that the people are in control when they can talk to the computer in their own natural language rather than having to adapt to the machine's language. Indeed, some of the computers used in artificial intelligence research can now adapt themselves to humans in a limited way rather than having humans adapt to them.

Teaching machines to recognize human speech involves the work of a number of different kinds of specialists, all working in the field of artificial intelligence. Speech scientists, psychologists, linguists, and computer scientists are among those who are working together to learn more about natural-language understanding.

One of the reasons for the difficulty in communicating directly with a computer is the fact that people use far more information than just sound waves in order to understand what they hear. Programming a computer to "understand" word sequences involves more than just the relationship of words. It involves knowledge and reasoning about the nature of the real world.

Scientists at a number of artificial intelligence centers are directing their research toward the goal of supplying background so that computers can draw inferences. The human brain does this so easily that one is seldom aware of it. For example, you may remark that you have a scratchy throat and had to go to two stores before you got relief. Almost everyone knows that you went to drug stores or places that carried medication, but a computer never had a sore throat. Nor has a computer ever been in a drug store.

At Yale University's Artificial Intelligence Project, computer scientists have programmed their machines to read stories and respond to them, with some rather amazing results. The project, under the direction of Dr. Roger C. Schank, is based on first understanding how people think and then making computers more intelligent by following the human model. They believe that people are the best models of intelligent behavior and they emphasize the fact that people are good at predicting the contents of what they will hear. People are not good at remembering large numbers of words. This makes it most practical for them to begin processing a sentence before it is finished.

New work in understanding natural language uses a different approach from the early work. About 20 years ago, many scientists were very excited about the idea of using computers to make translations from one language to another.

Early translation programs did most of their changing from one language to another by simple word-for-word substitution. About 80% of the translation could be done by storing a large number of words in a computer's memory along with a number of rules dealing with grammar and relationships. The machine could come up with a translation that might be tolerated if a human editor could later work it over. Some of the mistakes that the computers made are famous. For example, "The spirit is willing but the flesh is weak," was translated into the Russian text and then the text was retranslated back into English as "The wine is agreeable but the meat is spoiled." "Out of sight, out of mind," was translated into the Russian equivalent of "Blind and insane." These are just two examples that show that languages are filled with expressions based on special meaning.

There were a host of difficulties in machine-language translations. It seems evident that a large vocabulary stored in the memory of a computer along with detailed rules on word sequence and the speed to examine the context of ambiguous words are not enough to make meaningful and complete translations solely by means of computers.

However, research in creating computer programs that understand stories has been more successful. After discarding the idea that a computer could achieve some understanding by having all the possible meanings of a word stored in its memory, researchers moved toward understanding coherent text.

Individual sentences in isolation can have many meanings. Roger Schank suggests that to illustrate the many meanings of a sentence, one think about the following: "We saw the Grand Canyon flying to Chicago." A computer could not understand such a sentence without some knowledge about airplanes and geography. Think how it might interpret such a sentence!

Or think about the sentence, "The policeman stopped the car with his hand." Your brain fills in the details of a person driving the car, putting on the brakes, and stopping when a policeman holds up his hand at an intersection.

Roger Schank and others who work in the field of natural-language understanding note that computer language must be able to draw inferences if it is to mirror human language. According to Schank, people have two kinds of knowledge about the world they live in: general and specific. General knowledge enables people to understand and interpret the actions of others because all human beings have similar needs and standard ways of getting them fulfilled. Specific knowledge applies to situations that have been experienced many times, such as watching a television program, ordering food in a restaurant, buying a ticket to a show or game, and brushing one's teeth. In each case, the sequence of events that takes place is predictable. He suggests that much of human behavior depends on the learning of many scripts, or built-in knowledge of the world. The existence of common scripts makes it possible for people to draw inferences. These scripts can be considered as shorthand versions of everyday activities.

SAM (Script Applier Mechanism) is a system of computer programs that were written at the Yale University Artificial Intelligence Laboratory to make it possible to draw the inferences necessary to the understanding of stories. SAM processes stories in English, making some inferences as it does this. Restaurant stories are popular for showing SAM's ability to analyze the content and to answer questions.

An example of one of the simpler stories processed by SAM might be: "John went into a restaurant. He ordered a

Large space systems will require robots for fabrication, assembly, and construction in space. *—Jet Propulsion Laboratory*

hamburger. He paid the check and left." SAM recognizes this as a restaurant story and draws inferences about things that are obvious to people. If SAM is questioned, "What did John eat?" the answer will be "John ate a hamburger," even though this is not actually specified in the story. SAM knows that John probably ate what he ordered.

SAM can answer questions by drawing inferences about much more complicated stories. On a factual level, SAM understands the story even though it has never eaten a hamburger. A person who has experienced eating a hamburger might understand the story on a different level, but even humans are said to understand stories about things they never experienced. In reading a story, SAM constructs a scenario that contains the events mentioned and also that could be reasonably inferred to have happened.

SAM is like a person trying to read stories in great detail. In other words, it does not skim. FRUMP (Fast Reading Understanding and Memory Program) is a program based on the idea of a script, but its scripts are not as detailed as SAM's. FRUMP can keep track of scripts it has used and how it has used them, so it can process stories faster than SAM, although it does so more superficially.

FRUMP can process a story that is six or seven lines long from a newspaper and summarize it in several languages. Each summary is a one-line sentence telling the most important points of the story.

PAM (Plan Applier Mechanism) is another program that was developed at Yale. It understands stories by recognizing the plans of the characters in the stories and their goals. PAM makes predictions about what kinds of events may occur. Consider the following story that is often used in explaining what PAM can do:

> John wanted some money. He got a gun and walked into a liquor store. He told the owner he wanted some money. The owner gave John the money and John left.

If you ask the computer what John did at the liquor store, it will respond that he robbed it to get some money. If you ask why the owner gave John the money, the computer will respond that the owner was afraid that John would hurt him.

Does the computer know more about the story than it has been told? Is this an intelligent computer? PAM programmer Professor Robert Wilensky, now at the University of California at Berkeley, will explain that the computer simply incorporates a sense of how people analyze and reason. It recognizes the presence of a threat because it was asked a question in the realm of its understanding. It was programmed to recognize a gun as a threatening weapon.

If you told the computer that John took his gun into the store and that he was given money for the gun, PAM would conclude that he was selling his gun. Getting money for the gun triggers the relationship of exchanging an object for money and PAM is programmed to know that this infers selling, for PAM is goal-oriented.

BORIS (a Better Organized Reading and Inference System) is the first attempt to combine the abilities demonstrated in SAM and PAM. This research project by Michael G. Dyer and Wendy G. Lehnert combines the inference techniques of scripts, plans, goals, and themes in a single program of reading stories and answering questions about them. It, too, is part of the Yale Artificial Intelligence Project.

A story that was chosen for BORIS follows, along with questions that were asked after the story was put into the computer and the answers that the computer gave.

In the future, a small tethered robot may bring surface samples to a large automatic processing station on Mars. *—Jet Propulsion Laboratory*

THE KIDNAP STORY

(Courtesy of Yale University Department of Computer Science)

John left his office early Friday afternoon so he could attend a going-away party for his friend Bill. Bill had been transferred to California. When he arrived there were lots of people and plenty of beer. Three years ago Bill had borrowed $50 from John, which John hoped to get back before Bill left. He was about to remind Bill about it when he was called to the phone. It was his wife, Mary, and she was hysterical. Mary had just received a call from a stranger who claimed to have kidnapped their daughter Susan. He said he would call again. John told Mary to stay at home, keep off the phone, and wait until he got there. John drove home immediately. Just as he walked in the door, the phone rang. John picked it up. But it was only Karen, one of Mary's friends. John told her Mary was out and hung up. Mary wanted to call the police but John thought they should wait. They were discussing this when Susan walked in the door. She had stayed after school for a gymnastics meet and taken a late bus home. Nothing had happened to her. It was all a hoax.

****

Some representative BORIS questions and answers appear below. The questions are verbatim input to BORIS and the answers are verbatim computer output.

Q1: Why did John go to the party?
A1: He wanted to have a good time and he was Bill's friend and he wanted to get 50 dollars back from him.

Q2: Why did John leave the party?
A2: He was worried about Susan.

Q3: Why?
A3: Susan was kidnapped.

Q4: What happened to John at the party?
A4: He got a call from Mary.

Q5: Why did Mary call John at the party?
A5: She wanted to tell him about Susan's kidnapping.

Q6: Why did John want money from Bill?
A6: He borrowed 50 dollars from him.

Q7: Why didn't John talk to Bill?
A7: He was more worried about Susan.

Q8: Who called John at home?
A8: Karen.

Q9: Why?
A9: She wanted to talk to Mary.

Q10: Was Karen upset?
A10: No. She did not know about Susan's kidnapping.

Q11: Did John kidnap Susan?
A11: No. He was her father.

Q12: Where was Susan?
A12: She was attending a gymnastics meet.

Q13: What happened when Susan came home?
A13: John was relieved that she was safe.

Although the memory displayed by BORIS is indeed impressive, the researchers who developed this program point out that human memory is vastly superior to computer memory when dealing with episodes in the real world.

7.

STAYING IN CONTROL

How bright should computers be allowed to become? No matter whether or not you consider computers to be thinking machines, you cannot deny that they are becoming increasingly capable. If a computer as intelligent as the human brain could be built, should it be built? This is a question that is being asked by laymen and experts alike.

Certainly today's computers are a long way from being as intelligent as a human being. Both the human brain and the computer brain depend on input and output. They both process information and they both use energy. The human brain is far more compact than any computer that holds amounts of data. Within about three pounds of living matter, the brain houses between ten billion and a trillion or more bits of information. Every brain cell is directly connected to other brain cells with many connections, making possible a wealth of associations. The countless possible connections in the human brain makes it possible for a person to call on information from a rich store of past experiences. And the brain can handle thousands of tasks simultaneously.

While many people have said it is impossible to build a computer with anywhere near the capacity of the human brain, others claim that new developments will eventually make this possible. One of the limitations of computers has been the fact that they process information serially, not in parallel, and cannot summon up a wide variety of associations at one time. How can a computer make the many cross-connections necessary to think about all the details the human brain images when, for example, recalling a friend? Such a computer would need both tremendous capacity and the ability to call upon knowledge it has stored from past experience.

For every argument that a computer cannot be creative, experts suggest answers. Ways of simulating emotions mechanically have been explored. Can elements from separate programs be combined so that computers can draw from a massive amount of data and imitate the human brain much more successfully than the computers of today? No one knows the answers to such questions.

Almost everyone agrees that computer ability is changing rapidly. From vacuum tubes, transitors, and simple integrated circuits to "miracle chips," computers are said to have passed through four generations. This progress encompassed about 25 years. Computers are expected to pass from the fifth generation to the sixth generation by the end of this century. Some futurists predict that that is the time that the compactness and reasoning power of computers will begin to match that of the human brain.

Few disagree that a computer generation is shorter than a human generation, for the latter is considered to be about 20 years. If one was a child during the first generation of computers, he or she was only middle-aged by the fourth generation. In the cases of both humans and computers, in a

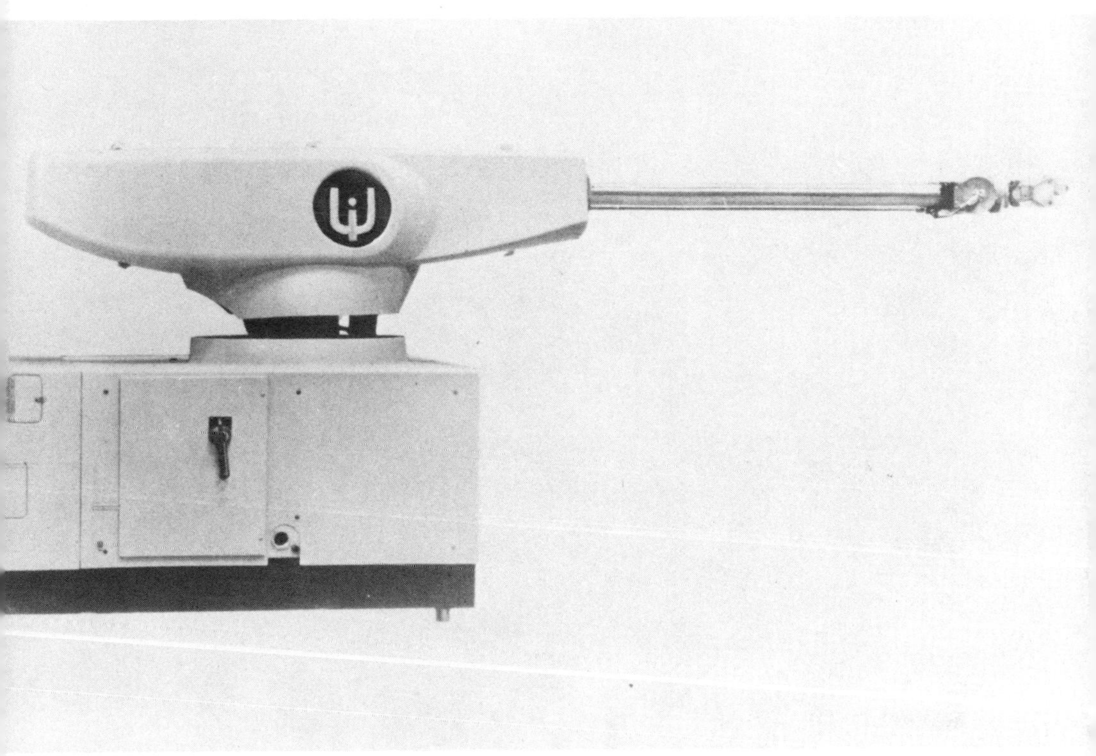

Computers are becoming increasingly sophisticated.
–Courtesy of Unimation, Inc.

sense, each generation produces the next one and passes some of its knowledge and experience along to the next generation. The brains of humans are not much different from one generation to the next. This is not the case with computers. Humans change computers so that each generation is more intelligent, or intelligent in a different way, than that of the parent generation.

Traditional computers have long surpassed people at high-speed mathematics and logic, but people are far superior at "common sense" kinds of operations and creativity. Computers that learn by experience, ask questions and answer them, and

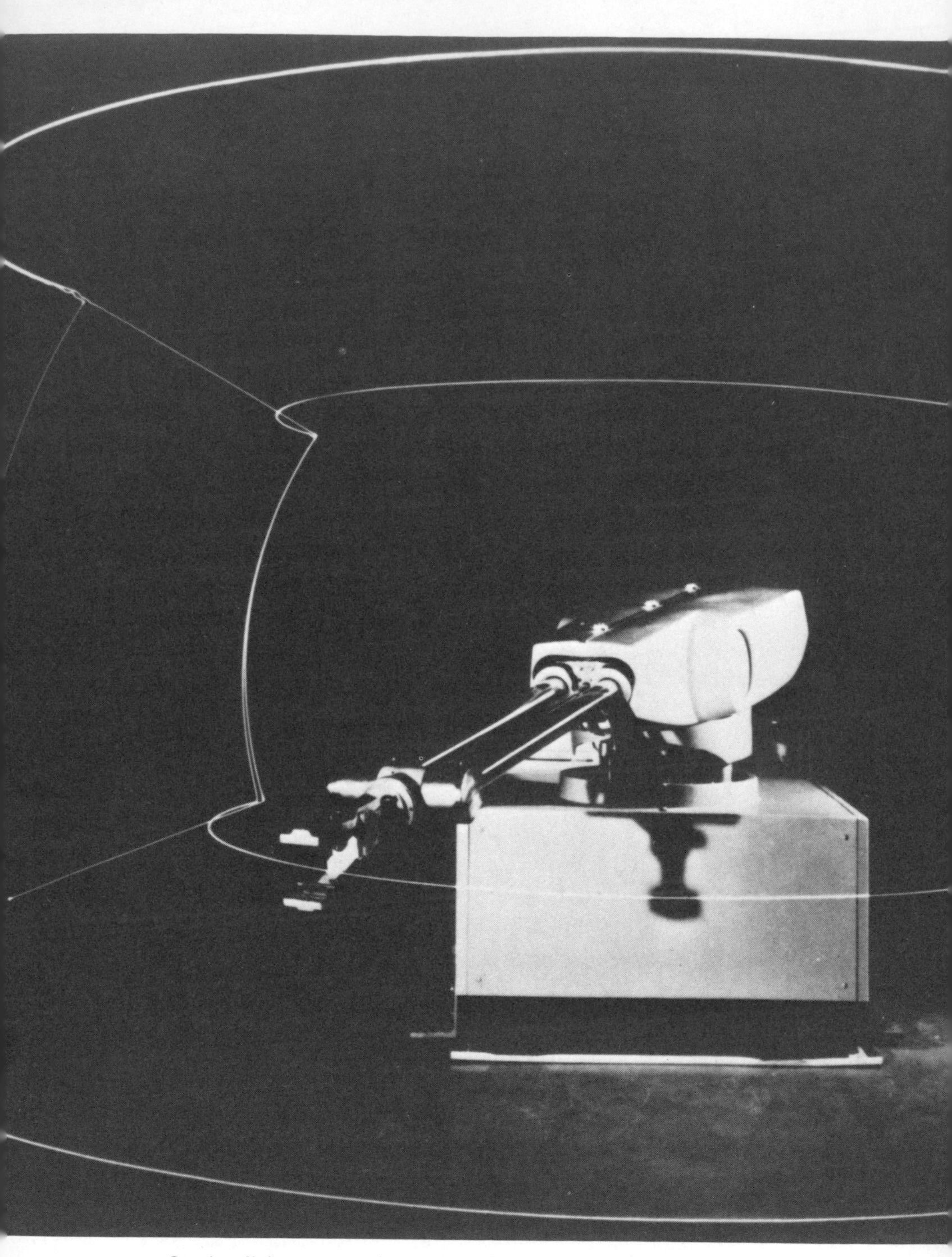

Strobe light traces the range of movement of the computer pictured on page 105. *–Courtesy of Unimation, Inc.*

those that create poetry and music are limited in their abilities. A computer that has the ability to decide what is relevent and what is not is very limited compared with the human brain.

Professor Edward A. Feigenbaum of Stanford University suggests that a computer program that would solve something of the nature of a Sherlock Holmes mystery would have to know everything about everything. He feels that scientists would never try to make such a machine. Not everyone agrees with him. As technology in artificial intelligence advances, more and more attention is being given to the question of what qualities intelligent machines should have. Some experts believe that qualities like selectivity should not even be granted to computers. Many believe that loneliness, fear, hate, love, and other emotions will always be beyond their scope.

While we are only in distant pursuit of intelligence that might simulate human intelligence in all its glory, a wide variety of people now are benefiting from the artificial intelligence research that has produced some programs exhibiting single aspects of it. Artificial intelligence is no longer considered to be a subject that is "blue sky," with little connection to the real world. Certainly, it has already accomplished part of its goal of making computers easier to use and more responsive to human needs. While trying to imitate the human brain, computer scientists may eventually learn things about the brain that we have not yet even thought of asking about.

One of the most practical and challenging of today's visions is in the development of telepersons, or surrogate workers for remote places, that have capabilities well beyond those of today's robots. The basic ideas for telepersons have already been worked out in a number of laboratories including M.I.T., Stanford, Edinburgh, and Carnegie-Mellon universities. Professor Marvin Minsky of the M.I.T. Artificial Intelligence

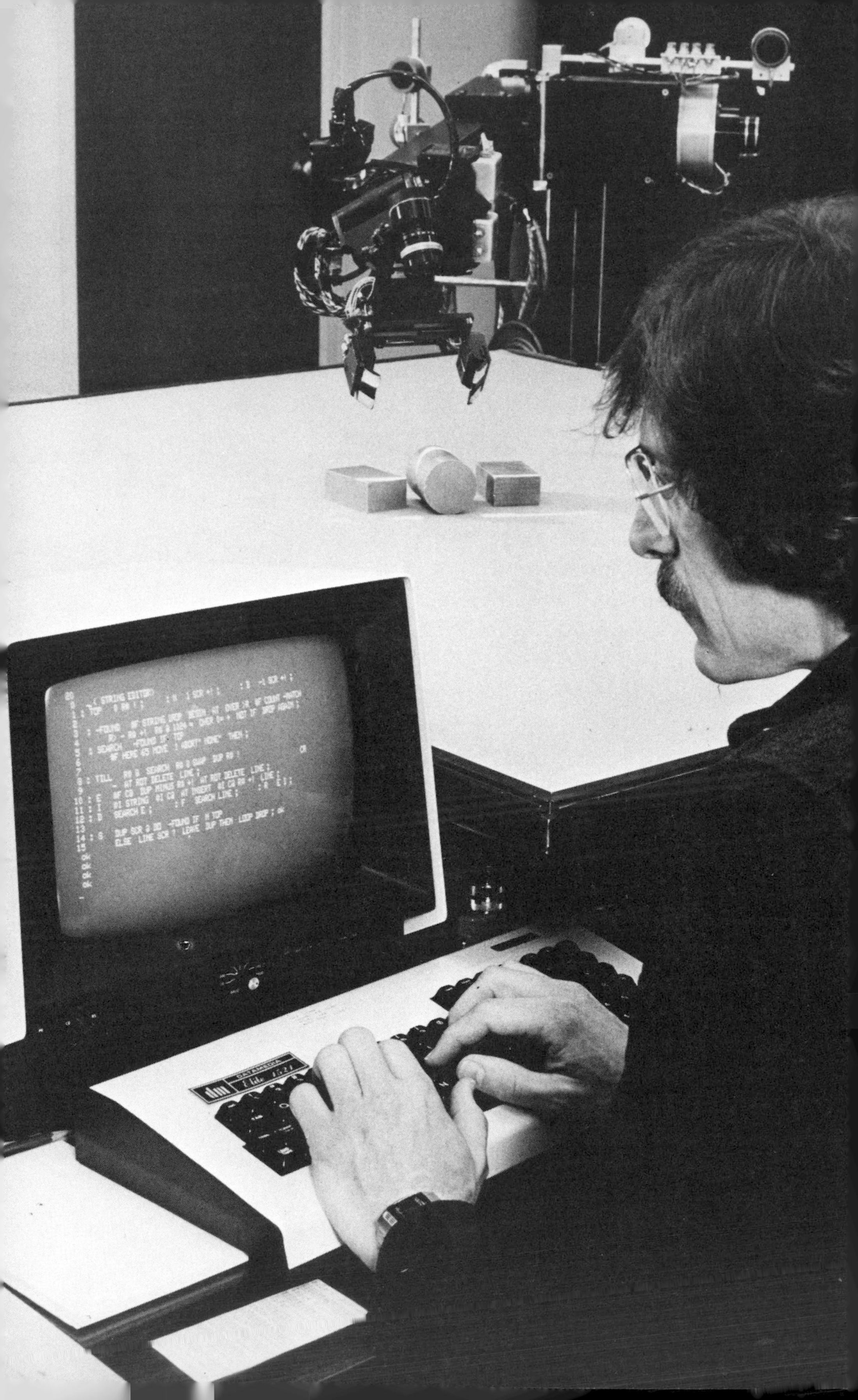
(STRING EDITOR)
DATAMEDIA

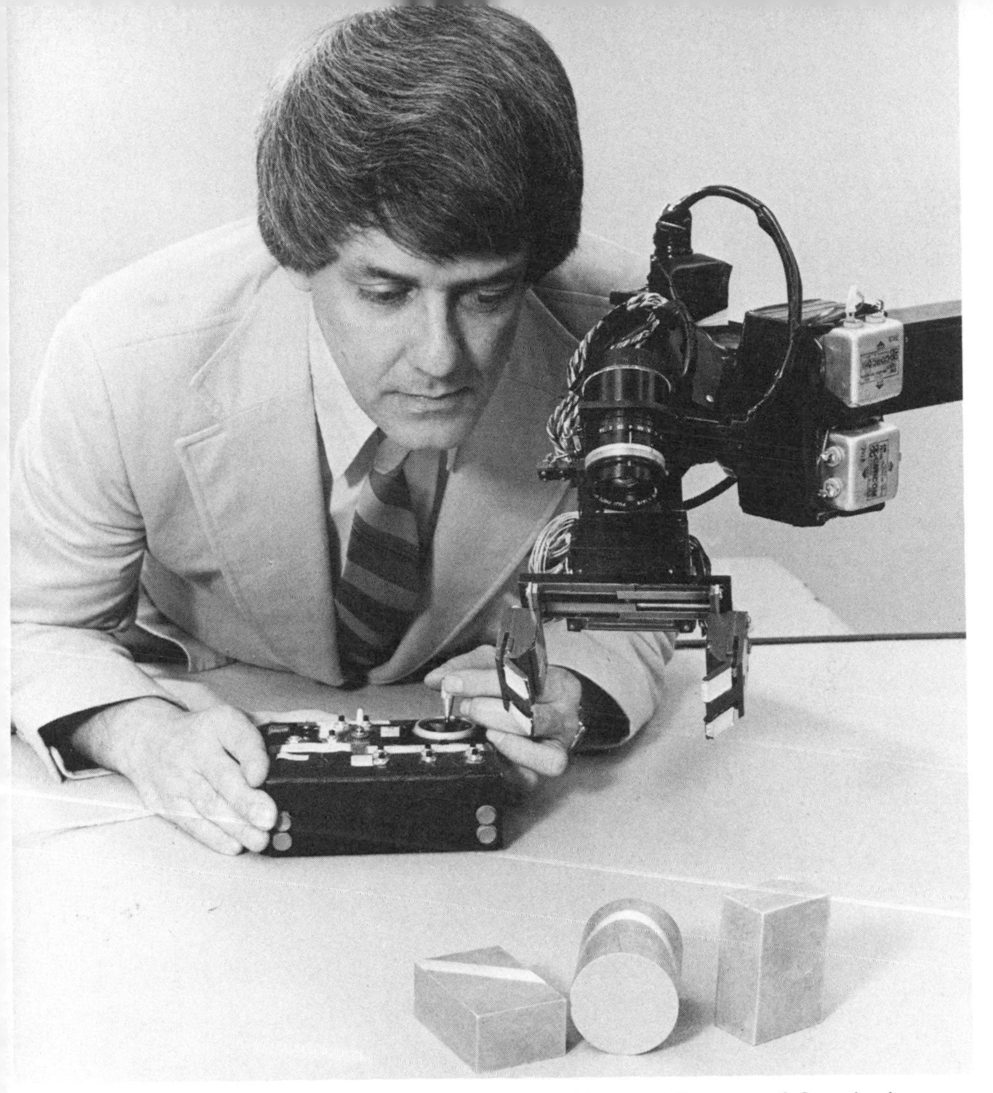

Above: James Albus, acting chief of the National Bureau of Standards Industrial Systems Division, with an experimental robot. The strobe light mounted just below the robot's "hands" illuminates objects in its field of vision with a narrow plane of light. A computer control deduces the rough shape and position of the objects from the image of this light plane as detected by the solid- state TV camera mounted above the wrist.

–Beamie Young, National Bureau of Standards

Opposite: Anthony Barbera of the National Bureau of Standards Industrial Systems Division at the programming console of an NBS experimental robot. Instrumentation on the robot includes a vision system and sonic sensors used as proximity detectors.

–Beamie Young, National Bureau of Standards

Laboratory describes a teleperson as one who could make dangerous jobs safe and comfortable. It could work in a nuclear reactor core, in the oceans depths, or deep in a mine. When teleperson instruments are perfected, each motion of a person's arm, wrist, and fingers will be transmitted to its mechanical counterpart, and signals from the teleperson's sensors will be returned so that the human will know exactly what is happening in the distance. Professor Minsky estimates that it will be ten to 20 years before such a vision can become a reality. Even this timetable will require both aggressive work on the technology and funding of about one billion dollars. He believes, however, that the results could shape a new world of improved health, energy, and security.

Practical applications of artificial intelligence are becoming more numerous even in today's world in spite of the opponents who claimed that few, if any practical applications could come from research in this field. One of the most exciting developments is in the area of expert systems.

Expert systems are designed by having computer specialists together with the best expert or experts in a special field, such as organic chemistry, explore the reasoning the expert uses to apply his or her knowledge. The programmers codify the expert knowledge and mimic it in the computer program. When, say, a chemist explains that an answer to a problem was obtained just through a feeling of what was right or wrong, the artificial intelligence researcher helps the expert to become better aware of the kind of thinking used in the problem solving.

One of the first expert systems is DENDRAL, a system that used knowledge obtained from Joshua Lederberg, the famous geneticist. Developed at Stanford University in California, this system helps organic chemists determine the molecular structure of unknown compounds. In this and other expert

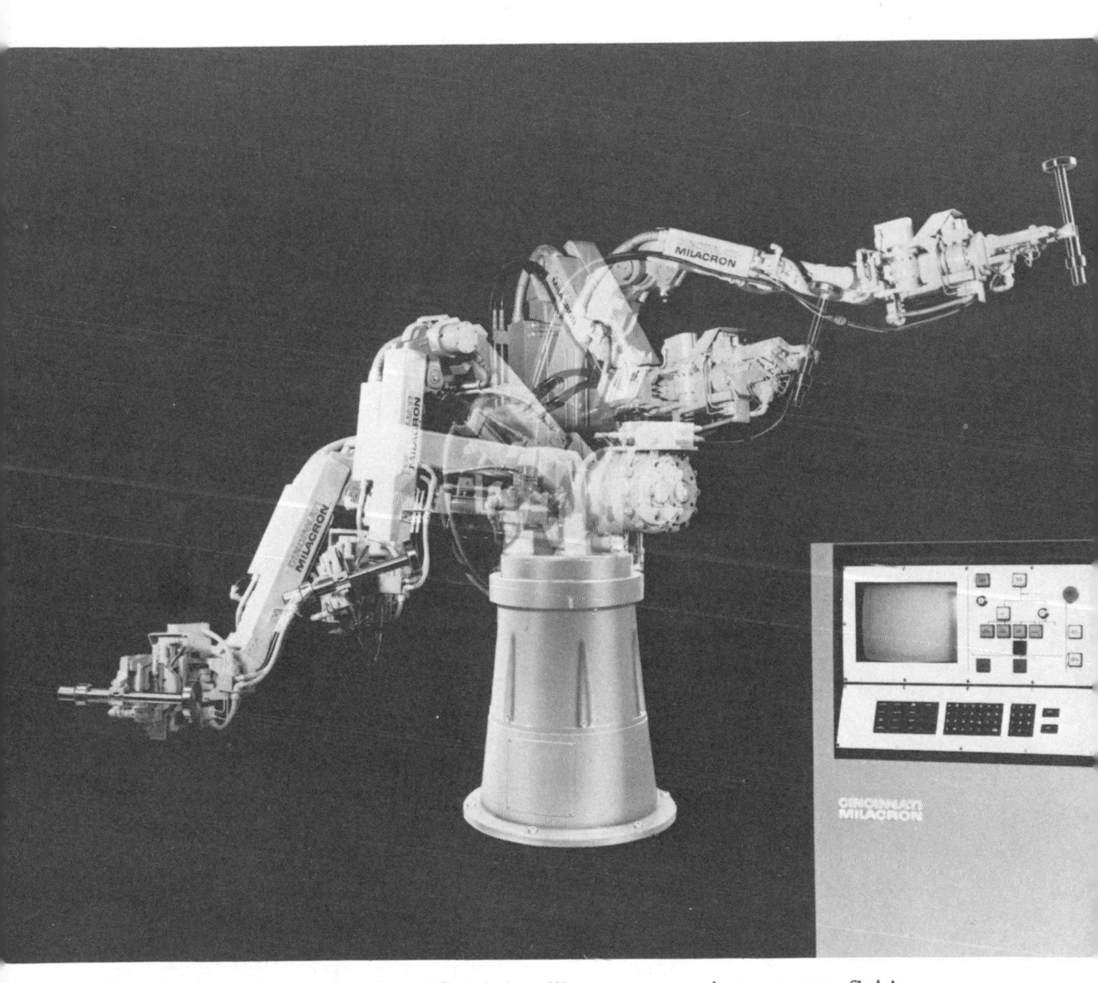

Practical applications of artificial intelligence extend to many fields including chemical research and medical diagnosis.

—Courtesy of Cincinnati Milacron

systems, the computer learns to solve problems in the special area. After the computer has learned to solve problems by being a student of the experts, it can act as a teacher to human pupils.

Expert systems already are being used in the manipulation of DNA, to assist in the prospecting for oil, in interpreting standard laboratory measures of pulmonary functions, and in a number of other situations. MYCIN, for example, is an expert system that simulates a medical consultant who specializes in infectious diseases. It engages in question-and-answer conversations with doctors who want special help with the identification of microogranisms and the prescription of antibiotic drugs. It also provides explanations of its advice and can supply "ifs," "whys," and so forth. MYCIN allows doctors to make improvements in its program by accepting information about special cases, such as that a drug is not suitable for a person with a rare allergy. This ability of being able to learn implies some mastery of the problems it discusses.

MYCIN is considered especially important in the field of artificial intelligence because it can possibly be used for general-purpose programs rather than just in the specialized areas of expert systems.

Professor Donald Michie of the Machine Intelligence Unit at the University of Edinburgh believes that expert systems may be the answer to the problem of letting people question a computer on why it reached a decision. Traditionally, computers are "number crunchers" or "information sifters." For example, most computer chess programs rely on what is called brute force, a method in which they just churn quickly through all possible moves and use their high-speed processing ability to weigh options rather than using the trial-and-error type of reasoning that humans use to make decisions.

Since expert systems reach conclusions through a process of reasoning that is like human reasoning (one that is based on logic and experience) they may provide a "human window." In these systems, people can understand the reasoning behind computer results. Professor Michie warns that such a window is needed to provide humans with a way of staying in command. In other words, this is the kind of artificial intelligence that will provide a way to monitor and control machine behavior. When computers arrive at conclusions through brute force, they do so with a speed and complexity that is beyond human comprehension.

Professor Michie gives an example of the bad consequences that can result when there is no "human window": there was much confusion and delay during Three Mile Island's nuclear mishap when people could not quickly understand the meaning of computer-controlled alarm systems.

Many artificial intelligence researchers stress the importance of remaining in control by making certain that programs can examine their own behavior and tell humans how they reach their conclusions. They point out that machines must not be given authority without responsibility.

Some scientists believe that there is less danger in the possibility of machines taking over than there is in humans becoming dependent on machines. Controversy continues on many fronts.

While some experts claim that some systems already surpass human intelligence, others claim that they never will. Some look ahead to a new relationship between computers and people in which they are completely dependent on each other for survival. Others point out computer limitations—things they never will be able to do.

Even the definition of artificial intelligence is a subject

of controversy. Several scientists have noted that the definition changes as research moves forward. For example, computer vision, once regarded as a part of artificial intelligence research, now is seen by many people as part of general computer development. Larry Tessler is credited as being the first to suggest that artificial intelligence is "whatever hasn't been done yet." Perhaps this is because of the fact that once a mental function is programmed, people tend to stop considering it as an essential ingredient of thinking. But for those who are willing to accept a limited definition of the word "intelligence," artificial intelligence has arrived.

Will the computer become a Joseph Golem? Are there things machines should not be allowed to do? Will humans remain in control?

If scientists proceed with caution and healthy fear, there is more reason to believe that intelligent machines will become powerful allies than that they will become man's enemies. In any case, the search for artificial intelligence goes on.

Computers of all sizes are becoming more accessible every day.

–Courtesy of Beaver College, Glenside, PA.

SUGGESTED READING

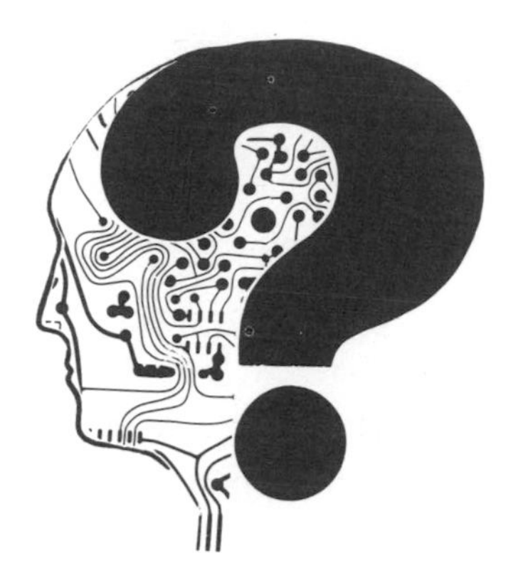

Boden, Margaret A. *Artificial Intelligence and Natural Man.* New York: Basic Books, 1977.

Dertouzos, Michael, and Joel Moses, Eds. *The Computer Age: a Twenty Year View.* Cambridge, Mass.: The MIT Press, 1979.

Dreyfus, Hubert. *What Computers Can't Do: A Critique of Artificial Reason.* New York: Harper and Row, 1972.

Evans, Christopher. *The Micro Millenium.* New York: The Viking Press, 1979.

Graham, Neil. *Artificial Intelligence.* Blue Ridge Summit, Pa: TAB Books, 1979.

Herbert, Frank, with Max Barnard. *Without Me You're Nothing: The Essential Guide to Home Computers.* New York: Simon and Schuster, 1980.

Hofstadter, Douglas R. *Godel, Escher, Bach: An Eternal Golden Braid.* New York: Basic Books, 1979.

Jackson, Philip C. *Introduction to Artificial Intelligence.* New York: Petrocelli Books, 1974.

Kent, Ernest. *The Brains of Men and Machines.* New York: McGraw-Hill, 1981.

Koff, Richard M. *Home Computers: A Manual of Possibilities.* New York: Harcourt Brace Jovanovich, 1979.

Landers, Richard R. *Man's Place in the Dybosphere.* Englewood Cliffs, N.J.: Prentice Hall, 1967.

McCorduck, Pamela. *Machines Who Think: A Personal Inquiry into the History and Prospects of Artificial Intelligence.* San Francisco: W. H. Freeman, 1979.

Osborne, Adam. *Running Wild: The Next Industrial Revolution.* Berkeley, C.A.: Osborne/McGraw-Hill, 1979.

Restak, Richard. *The Brain: The Last Frontier.* Garden City, N.Y.: Doubleday and Company, 1979.

Ringle, Martin. *Philosophical Perspectives in Artificial Intelligence.* Atlantic Highlands, N.J.: Humanities Press, 1979.

Weizenbaum, Joseph. *Computer Power and Human Reason: From Judgment to Calculation.* San Francisco: W. H. Freeman, 1976.

Winston, Patrick H. *Artificial Intelligence.* Reading, Mass.: Addison-Wesley, 1977.

INDEX

A

B

C

D

E

V